CW00959776

THE LIBRARY
H.M. CUSTOMS AND EXCISE

LIVERPOOL CENTRAL DOCKS

1799–1905

An Illustrated History

ADRIAN JARVIS

ALAN SUTTON

NATIONAL MUSEUMS & GALLERIES
· ON MERSEYSIDE ·

First published in the United Kingdom in 1991
Alan Sutton Publishing Ltd · Phoenix Mill · Far Thrupp · Stroud
Gloucestershire
and National Museums and Galleries on Merseyside

First published in the United States of America in 1992
Alan Sutton Publishing Inc · Wolfeboro Falls · NH 03896–0848

British Library Cataloguing in Publication Data

Jarvis, Adrian
Liverpool Central Docks
1799–1905.
I. Title
387.15

ISBN 0–86299–783–6

Library of Congress Cataloging in Publication Data applied for

Typeset in Times 10/12.
Typesetting and origination by
Alan Sutton Publishing Limited.
Printed in Great Britain by
The Bath Press, Bath, Avon.

CONTENTS

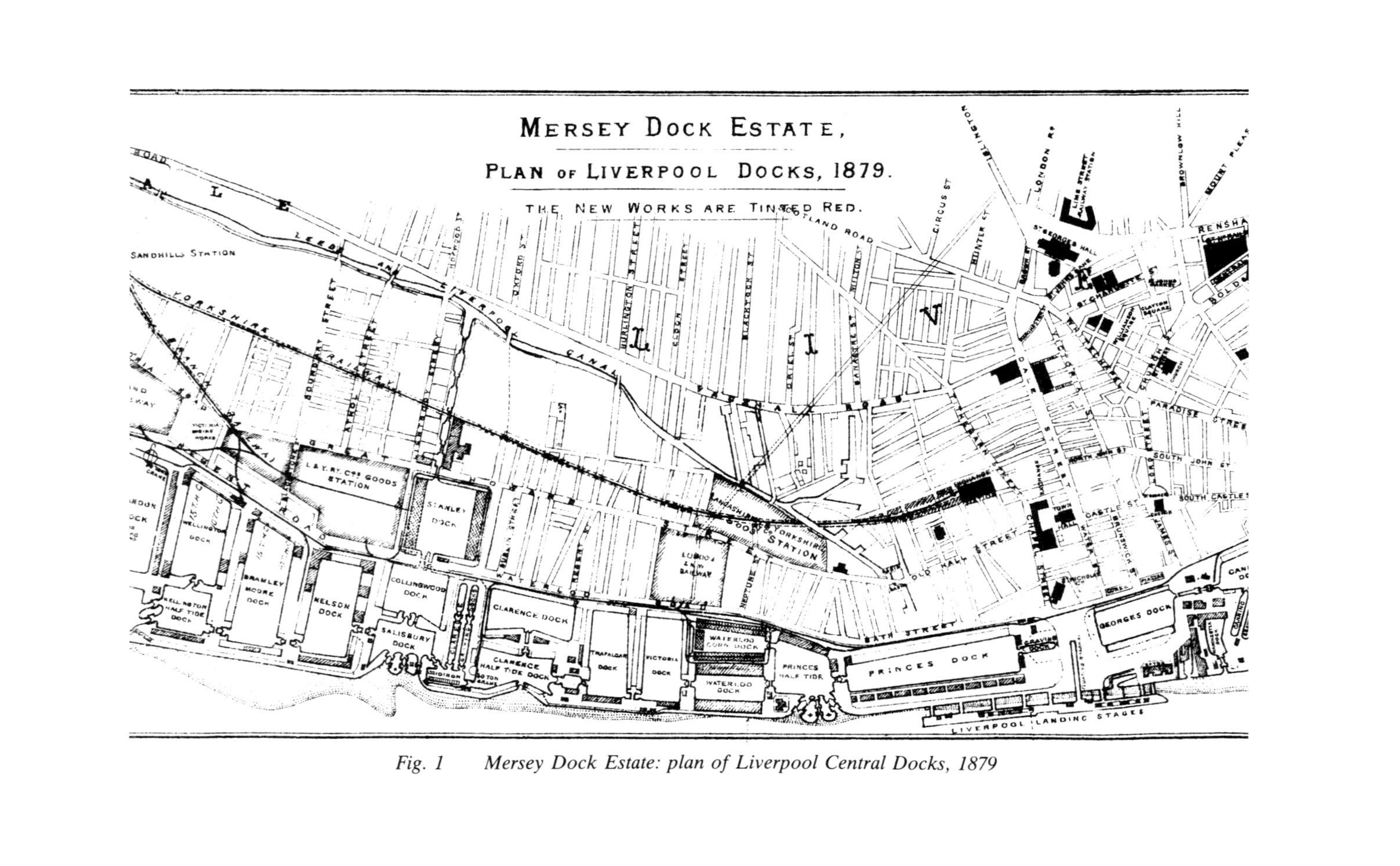

Fig. 1 Mersey Dock Estate: plan of Liverpool Central Docks, 1879

PREFACE

In early 1989, the Merseyside Development Corporation commissioned National Museums and Galleries on Merseyside to undertake an historical survey of the recent extension to their designated area. Its purpose was to identify and record buildings and structures of historic interest, to provide information and advice on conservation issues and to publish research findings. Merseyside Maritime Museum provided accommodation and office services and seconded the author of the present work as survey manager and the commission fee from the Development Corporation enabled the appointment of a research assistant, an illustrator and a data clerk on two-year contracts.

The survey has produced a number of papers for learned journals, and has established a joint imprint with a local publisher for the production of a series of booklets on fairly specific topics within the field. Some of these Merseyside Port Folios will be found cited in the notes of the present work.

While the Development Corporation was primarily concerned in the short term with the risk that it might destroy historic material simply because it was not recognized, it was also their intention that the survey should make some sort of contribution to scholarship, and it is with that hope that this book has been produced.

In 1984, Nancy Ritchie-Noakes published *Liverpool's Historic Waterfront*, which was the end product of a previous Development Corporation-supported survey. At the time it set a new standard which others have sought to follow. This book, however, deals with a different area and addresses different questions. Quite a large proportion of the South Docks was, at some stage in its history, at the sharp end of technological development, and one or two of those docks were still capable of handling quite large modern ships in 1972. The material remains within the area thus provided evidence of a very long evolutionary sequence of change and development extending over more than two centuries. The Central Docks, which form the subject of the present work, have a very different outline to their history. Some were in the forefront of technology when they were new, but were rapidly overtaken by the increasing size of ships, while others could only be considered as second rate from the start.

The material remains in the Central Docks were therefore of a completely different nature to those in the south. Some, such as the Waterloo Corn Warehouses, were of definite technological interest, but many, such as the north-west Princes sheds, were of interest only in the way that they illustrated a piecemeal policy of attempting to modernize obsolete facilities with visibly inadequate funding. Yet, as everybody knows, the Port of Liverpool was one of the nineteenth century's greatest success stories. The questions posed by the physical remains were not, therefore 'what?' as in the South Docks, but 'how?' and above all, 'why?'

The way in which the Mersey Docks and Harbour Board chose to neglect this group of docks for so long seems so strange that much of this book has been concerned to find out how and why it happened. It appeared at an early stage that very little work had been done in two particular fields: those of what actually happened on the ground during the building and operation of docks and of how decisions were made at top management level. These were the factors which seemed to hold the key to a considerable historical problem, and in their investigation much emerged which had not appeared in the pages of earlier authors none of whom had tackled the specifics of the Central Docks either. Much of the second half of last century was dogged with engineering problems and errors and the Board and its standing committees frequently failed to make effective policies and have these implemented. By the end date of this book, the Board was in desperate financial trouble, and because this state of affairs and its causes have not been generally recognized, neither has the fact that in 1905 the Board had recently undergone such a change of attitude that it would be able to back cautiously away from the precipice and then finance the magnificent Gladstone Dock system.

PREFACE

To the reader who hopes to find a bolt-by-bolt account of everything left on the ground in the Central Docks in 1990, the author offers his apologies, together with the hope that the rather different approach adopted may prove to be of at least equal interest.

ACKNOWLEDGEMENTS

Although the production of a book of this kind was only a secondary objective of the Port Survey, and much of the information in it was originally gathered and indexed for other purposes, the credit for any contribution to scholarship which this work makes is due to the Trustees of National Museums and Galleries on Merseyside and to Merseyside Development Corporation. Without the staff time they made available for the project, the work would have taken at least five years longer than it did.

My colleagues in the Port Survey team have been a source of help in many ways: Ken McCarron with references, suggestions and discussion of ideas; Samantha Ball saved thousands of words of tedious explanation with her line illustrations and Sandra Page laboured long to transform the draft into a state where someone else could understand it, patiently taking on board my numerous changes of heart along the way.

Like most authors, I have been a source of constant problems for the staff of various institutions, notably the Maritime Record Centre, The Liverpool Record Office and the Sydney Jones Library of Liverpool University, I offer my thanks for their help. David Flower, Museum Photographer, Colin Pitcher, freelance photographer and John Calderbank, photographer in Liverpool City Engineer's Reprographic Department, have produced material to short deadlines made necessary by my preoccupation with the text.

Not being an engineer, I depended heavily in some places on advice from the professionals, and particularly Ken Smith, Lecturer in Civil Engineering at Liverpool University and Roger Rumbold, Chief Engineer of Merseyside Development Corporation. Arthur Davies,

Museum Technician, who served his time in the old school of engineering fitting, was a source of much verbal information about the way things were done and made.

My wife Anthea, was not only a source of encouragement but also read much of the draft material to try and help render it comprehensible. She also provided material for Chapter Eight and tolerated the invasion of her end of the study by my piles of paper.

Dr Gordon Jackson read the draft at what was the most inconvenient time of the academic year and provided many helpful comments as well as finding time to discuss them. Any errors which remain are my responsibility. He was kind enough to remark that few studies in dockland history have got down to such a level of detail, and the credit for that is due to the man who ensured that the massive Mersey Docks & Harbour Board Archive was preserved in a public depository, namely Albert Nute, formerly assistant secretary to the Mersey Docks and Harbour Company.

MEASUREMENTS

1 Money

British pre-decimal currency divided the pound into 20 shillings (s) and a shilling into 12 pence (d). The guinea was a long-running archaism worth 21 shillings.
1 shilling = 5 new pence
1 penny = 0.42 new pence

2 Area

1 acre = 4,840 square yards
1 sq.yd = 0.836 square metres
1 acre = 0.405 hectares

3 Heights & Depths

The datum used was the level of the sill of Liverpool's first (1715) dock, known as Old Dock Sill (ODS) or occasionally Old Dock Datum. Measurements above and below ODS were in feet and inches.
1 foot = 0.305 metres
12 inches = 1 foot
1 inch = 25.4 millimetres

4 Distance

1 mile = 1,609 metres
1,760 yards = 1 mile
1 yard = 0.914 metres
3 feet = 1 yard

5 Volume

1 bushel = 8 gallons = 36.4 litres

CHAPTER ONE

The Early Development Of The Port

The circumstances which led to Liverpool constructing the country's first commercial wet dock, opened in 1715, have long been well known and much published, as has the success of the venture and the accelerating demand for additional dock space which followed. In so far as any weakness existed in the historical coverage, it lay only in the fact that later works tended to derive from earlier ones, which could lead to the repetition and perpetuation of errors. Rideout, for example, pointed out a simple yet clangorous error committed by Picton in transcribing a date wrongly which was then repeated by both Gomer Williams and Ramsay Muir. The sentence in which the error occurred began in all three accounts with the words 'Thus encouraged . . .',[1] a degree of unanimity which would surely attract the notice of any schoolmaster marking examination papers. The time was ripe for a new account which went back to the primary sources, and this arrived in the shape of Ritchie-Noakes' *Liverpool's Historic Waterfront* (1984). This publication weeded out many errors and provided much which had not appeared in print before, to the point where it may justly be claimed that it is superfluous to re-tread that ground here.

There have, however, been problems of emphasis in interpretation. Although it was pointed out in the 1950s that the triangular trade between Liverpool, the Sankey and the Weaver was probably as important as another, rather better-known, triangular trade, still the popular perception of the growth of eighteenth-century Liverpool is that it was very largely funded by the Slave Trade. Documentary evidence for this view appears to be limited to the celebrated utterance of a drunken actor, to the effect that every brick of the detestable town was 'cemented by the blood of a negro'. More sober views have, over the years, come down to a sort of consensus that average profits in the Slave Trade were probably between 10 and 15 per cent. This figure would not be excessive for such a high-risk trade even if one did not have to allow for huge variations in fortune on different ventures. The prominent slave-trader William Davenport made about 8 per cent overall during the period 1757–84, but of sixty-two ventures, twenty-two made a loss, two of those losses were of over 40 per cent. On the credit side one venture made an astonishing profit of over 80 per cent, but eleven made profits below 10 per cent.[2]

It would be equally wrong to deny that the Slave Trade was important to Liverpool. It has sometimes been deduced from the hindsight evidence that Liverpool's trade increased even faster after the abolition of the Slave Trade than it did before it, that the importance of the trade was a myth propagated only by the (implicitly highly evil) men involved in it. This argument entirely misses the point, for any entrepreneur worth his profit had identified the risk of the trade being abolished well in advance, and had diversified his activities accordingly. The importance of the Slave Trade to Liverpool was that it formed a way of turning over very large sums of money, the comparatively moderate percentage return on which still represented substantial amounts available for re-investment in the town.

For those to whom the Slave Trade was insufficiently exciting, there was privateering. Britain was at war for, in round figures, half the eighteenth century and followed a fairly established pattern of beginning a war with the Royal Navy in a state of total unpreparedness. In most cases the Navy eventually got itself organized and achieved effective control of whichever water was in dispute, but until it did that, there were profits to be made by privateering. There are two ways of looking at privateering: a privateer was a gallant and patriotic naval auxiliary; he was also a licenced pirate. The two views are by no means mutually exclusive, and there is no reason to deny that a successful privateer was motivated both by patriotism and profit. The risks were obviously high, but the profits could be spectacular. Perhaps the most celebrated was the taking of *Carnatic* by

Captain Dawson of the *Mentor* in October 1778. The value of the prize was £135,000. Even more spectacular was the value of the French East Indiaman *Liberté* taken in 1793 by the *Pilgrim*, estimated as £190,000. As in the case of the Slave Trade, the importance is not so much in the detail of financial returns as in the arrival in Liverpool of large amounts of money available for investment. In 1779 the town was recorded as having 120 privateers whose collective booty amounted to over £1,000,000.[3]

Prize money, however, only enriched individuals or companies. It did not guarantee the availability of funds for dock construction or improvement. There were those, notable among them Mathew Gregson, who favoured the establishment of joint-stock companies for dock construction and some of his considerable wealth came from privateering. The precedent, however, was that docks had been built by the Dock Trustees and, despite apparent changes in organization, that was really how it remained until the time of the Mersey Docks & Harbour Board, constituted in 1857.

The most perfunctory perusal of the evidence gathered by the Municipal Commissioners prior to the passage of the Municipal Reform Act of 1835[4] will serve to show that most of local government nationwide was, at best, ill-attuned to the demands made on it and, at worst, effete and corrupt in fairly equal proportion. Perhaps the most telling conclusion in the monumental work of Sidney and Beatrice Webb is that there was no such thing as a 'local government system'. Under the terms of its Charter, the Liverpool Common Council was a 'close' body, i.e. one to which members were appointed only by co-option, on which there was a permanent Tory and Anglican majority. Almost any device which occurs to the modern mind as a 'corrupt' practice which might arise in modern local government, be it bribery, nepotism, use of insider information, conflict of interest or just shameless junketing, was not merely there to be seen, but was regarded as the normal way of business. There were, of course, those in Liverpool who struck a higher moral tone, but it is probably no coincidence that they were nearly all dissenters of one denomination or another, and thus ineligible for election to the Council until the repeal of the Test & Corporation Acts in 1828.[5]

The purpose in drawing attention to the nature of unreformed borough government is not to invite anachronistic moral outrage but to make it clear that many boroughs would have been incapable of taking any effective action to build, maintain or operate any significant corporate asset, much less anything of the size and complexity of a dock estate. What might loosely be called the machinery of local government had evolved in a different age, and for different purposes.

The Liverpool Corporation may seem corrupt by some later standards, but by the standards of its day it was a model of diligence, efficiency and open government. It kept minutes of its meetings and compiled and made available audited accounts of its revenue. While it might be taking matters too far to imply that it felt any responsibility to 'the public' it is certainly reasonable to suggest that it felt a corporate responsibility for the general well-being of the town. Technically, the members of a corporation were responsible only to each other and the wider view taken by the Liverpool Councillors shows that they were not only ahead of their time, but indeed in some respects forming a model which would be adopted in the course of future reform.

In one important respect the Liverpool Corporation Estate caused the adoption of methods which would only later become widespread elsewhere, and this was the employment of salaried officers. As the Webbs pointed out, this was in many places a distinguishing mark of the reformed borough, but in Liverpool the scale of operation and the problems it caused had long since steered the borough in that direction. The work of John Foster in implementing the provisions of the 1785 Liverpool Improvement Act was not merely that of an expert officer, but really that of a proto-Town Planning Officer. By 1816, the financial management of the estate had become somewhat chaotic, and Charles Okill was given the demanding task of sorting it out. The work he did was roughly analogous to that of a modern management consultancy, but his status was that of a salaried Corporation Officer. Some officers were also entitled to take on private work, and indeed John Foster Junior was paid a commission on major works designed for the Corporation in addition to his substantial salary of £1,000 p.a. The key to the Corporation's operation on such a large scale was a deal done in the seventeenth century.[6]

Historically the Lordship of the Manor was the property of the Molyneux family (later Earls of Sefton) and had been the subject of niggling disputes for some time. These could all be very roughly characterized as conflict between traditional land title on the one hand and the wealth and acumen of a very thrusting little business community on the other. Matters came to a head in 1671 when Lord Molyneux, having laid out and built along Lord Street, started to construct a bridge over the pool. His workers were repelled by force, and after a certain amount of further wrangling, agreement was reached whereby the Corporation leased the fee-farm and most of the other rights within the town of Lord Molyneux, for the sum of £30 per year for a thousand years. The agreement, of 14 and 15 September 1672, is not the dusty bit of local constitutional history it might first appear, but the basis of Liverpool's extraordinary growth over the next century and a half.

By this agreement, the Corporation acquired nearly 1,000 acres of land. This not only gave them autonomy, it also gave them significant revenue as the growth of the town ensured consistent pressure for new building. Eventually, even the Mosslake Fields, which had belonged to the Corporation since 1309, would become the site for substantial and expensive merchant housing: by such standards the land down in the town was of almost incalculable value to the future of the town.

In the short term, the land was possibly less important than the rights that came with it to levy Town Dues, on goods passing through the port. These were quite distinct from and additional to Dock Dues and Port Dues and meant that investment in docks produced a return not only in the coffers of the Dock Trustees, but of the Corporation as well. In addition, the dues could, if necessary, be used as loan security to raise capital for large ventures, whether in the docks or elsewhere. In the longer term, though, it was the land which was important, and perhaps the first manifestation of that importance was in the building of the early docks, for the land acquired included both sides of the pool and a stretch of land and foreshore to either side of its mouth.

The growth of trade and population which was facilitated by the development of the early docks, small as they were, made town improvement a matter of some urgency. The streets of central Liverpool in 1780 were the streets of a small fishing village with a population of a few hundred. To that population had been added not just a growing number of successful merchants and shipowners along with their employees, but the beginnings of manufacturing industries and a substantial infrastructure of port services. Moss's *Guide to Liverpool* of 1796 generally sets out to convey a pleasant impression of the town, but even with that intention and writing after considerable recent improvement, Moss had still to mention the vast quantity of smoke emitted from the saltworks 'which makes it very offensive' and advise visitors to pass the Oil House on the windward side as the smell is 'very disagreeable even at some distance' downwind. Because ships were small, numerous and comparatively unseaworthy by later standards the number of shipwrights in the town ran into thousands, and they were paralleled by a small army of practitioners of other maritime trades like sail-making, blacksmithing and rigging. Eighteenth-century packaging methods made employment for coopers, crate-makers, basket-makers and bag-makers. As most goods were landed onto open quays, there was a good living for carters and wagoners, who in turn had their own infrastructure of

Aerial view from Victoria in the south to Nelson in the north, taken in 1933. Clarence has been filled, the Graving Docks rebuilt and Trafalgar massively remodelled, but Salisbury, Collingwood and Stanley remain much as they were in 1905
(Liverpool City Engineer's Department)

wheelwrights, farriers and ostlers. The fairly primitive methods available for loading and discharging cargoes meant that even before any problems with the weather were considered, a ship's stay in dock was likely to be of weeks rather than days, with the result that to the resident population was added a transient population of seamen.

All this activity supported a buoyant building trade which in turn provided demand for brick, stone, wood, glass and ironmongery. Finally, of course, all these people had to eat, a need which was reflected in the disgusting open-fronted slaughterhouses of Pool Lane (commemorated until recently in the name of a public house in Fenwick Street) and in the pollution problems associated with urban cow and pig-keeping.

The result was a town which through much of its extent was quite inconceivably nasty and dirty. If the reader has any picture of late eighteenth-century towns in which reflections of the poetry of William Roscoe, the music of Vivaldi or the fine houses of Bath lurk in the background, perhaps it is worth explaining how one could replicate the conditions on the streets of downtown Liverpool in about 1780.[7] Let us imagine a small and very cramped village like Mousehole in Cornwall. Into it we must transport a couple of hundred tons of assorted human and animal excrement, some to be spread over the streets, some left in heaps awaiting the attention of the scavengers. Now we scatter quantities of waste products of various trades around, including blood and unspeakable fluids from livestock trades. Next, add the traffic, in the form of a hundred or two horse-drawn carts engaged in competition probably as dangerous as it was foul-mouthed with the occasional stage-coach or wagon. Finally, the pedestrians, to the extent of a fair-sized football crowd. Among them will be drunks, pickpockets, muggers and con-men. If our imaginary eighteenth-century Liverpool theme park is beginning to sound unlovely, remember that we have yet to add the delights of the judicial system, featuring public whipping of women, the hanging of the rotting corpses of felons in chains for months [8] and occasional executions for such serious offences as cutting the bindings of hop plants. In times of shortage of 'hearts of oak' the Press Gang added its legalized mayhem to the scene. Yet even this does not quite plumb the depths of nastiness, for the streets of Mousehole which we used for our starting point are paved, drained and lit. Most of the streets of 1780 Liverpool were not.

Within about fifty years, that is to say by the passing of the Municipal Reform Act, this hideous scene had been largely transformed. There were still areas which the genteel would be wise to avoid, and there were areas where housing conditions were quite as bad as anything that Engels later described in Manchester, but huge improvements had been effected in street paving and cleansing, drainage, water supply and street lighting. The really noxious trades had been shifted to the edge of the town. Mr Muspratt and his highly toxic chimney were eventually harried out of the town altogether.[9] While many of the improvements were carried out by private enterprise, the initiative behind them came largely from the corporation, backed by the revenues of the Corporation Estate and perhaps also by the traditional arm-twisting power which came with the ownership of land.

Massive expenditure was involved: the Improvement Commissioners appointed under the 1785 Improvement Act spent £150,000 in three years, mainly on street widening and paving and improvements to sewers. In most of the principal streets, quite strict 'planning constraints' were applied to proposed new buildings to ensure that no backsliding of standards took place. New public buildings were designed and constructed to very high standards and with comparatively little concern for cost. What was happening was a reflection of dock revenues which had multiplied more than forty times during half a century.

The growth of the Dock Estate had been equally stimulated by growing trades and revenues. Not only were new docks being added at an increasing rate, but the older docks were being modernized at the same time, and the iron rule of Jesse Hartley, Dock Engineer from 1824–60, ensured that inferior materials and methods went the same way as the corruption and inefficiency he found at the time of his appointment – out. While it was the work of Ritchie-Noakes which first established that Hartley was a great engineer, more recent work has perhaps made his pedestal even loftier as it has become clear that both John Foster before him and G.F. Lyster after him have tended in the past to be over-rated.[10]

The Central Docks were originally known as the North Docks, the division being the Pier Head at Georges Basin. In some ways it is strange that development did not progress even more markedly downstream, for the Pluckington Bank, which was the eventual killer of the South Docks when they closed in 1972, was already a problem at the beginning of last century, and was causing really serious difficulties by 1847. It is not even true to say that all the bigger new docks were to the north, for although this is true of Princes Dock, Salisbury and Collingwood were of quite modest size. To the south, Brunswick, opened in 1832, remained the biggest dock in the system for twenty years when it was surpassed by Huskisson.[11]

Princes Dock, opened in 1821, was intended as the flagship of the system, for the use of the largest ships visiting the port, most of which were in the North America trade. By the time it was opened, there was an incipient demand for berths for steamships, leaving the Dock Committee trapped between their justifiable dread of fires on the estate and their desire to serve and profit from any trade that was going. The result was that almost as soon as Princes was finished, and certainly before it was paid for, Hartley was charged with preparing a scheme for a single dock, separated from the others, for the accommodation of steamers only. This was, no doubt, a fine idea in some senses, but of course it would prevent other development of traditional sailing ship docks in the immediate vicinity. The policy soon began to slip, for in 1834, only four years after Clarence Dock was opened, Waterloo Dock brought sailing ships one step nearer to steam and in 1836 Victoria and Trafalgar Docks were completed, adjoining Clarence on the south and west sides. The surrounding of the supposedly isolated steam dock was completed in Hartley's *annus mirabilis* of 1848 when five docks were opened on the same day, Salisbury, Collingwood, Stanley, Nelson and Bramley-Moore.

Even Jesse Hartley made occasional errors of judgement, and one of these was that he was not as far ahead of changes in ship design as perhaps he might have been. The 1848 group of docks did not take sufficient account of the rapid increase in width of paddle steamers, and it was fortunate that shipping volume was growing at such a rate that he was readily able to catch up with the growth of ships, and eventually to build his 100 ft entrance at Canada which was more than sufficient to see out the age of the paddle steamer. He was backed by a Dock Committee which did not regard merely being the best as sufficient: dock followed dock in increasing size, and in the last fifteen years of Hartley's life the fruits of their cooperation increasingly out-distanced their competitors. What is significant in the present context is that until 1949, when the new Waterloo entrance was opened, there was no entrance into any of the docks from Princes to Bramley-Moore which could pass vessels of more than 60 ft beam. We cannot, of course, blame Hartley for the fact that his 'North' docks were not subjected to the same process of modernization and enlargement which he so successfully applied to many of the older and smaller docks, but the end result was that from about 1860 onwards the Central Docks ceased to take those traffics which used the largest vessels and gradually gravitated first to the smaller ocean trades and finally to coasting. By about 1890, they were totally outdated, and far from ideal even for coasting, with pokey, dark, obsolete sheds, little handling equipment and most of the movable bridges and gates still operated by hand. The old movable bridges were nearly all inadequate for rail traffic, with the result that cargo-handling away from the east quays had been improved little if at all since the opening of Princes Dock in 1821.

Waterloo Dock had been heavily rebuilt and modernized to provide specialized corn warehousing in a major scheme completed in 1868, and while the rapid improvement in bulk grain handling machinery meant that Lyster's installation was already obsolescent in 1890, the dock was functioning tolerably well, which was far more than could be said of the rest of the central system. There were frequent and not always amiable clashes between the Board and its customers, and sometimes within the Board itself, as to the relative priorities of building large new docks further downstream and modernizing the potentially useful acreage of smaller older docks. Eventually the 'modernizers' got their way, and an extensive scheme to turn the Central Docks into high quality specialist coasting berths was begun. While some of the work was a little penny-pinching, it nevertheless gave the Central Docks a new lease of life, and it is the completion of this scheme in 1905 which fixes the terminal date of this book.

A Brief Account of the Ownership and Management of the Docks

The construction of the first dock, while initially a venture by the Common Council, was undertaken largely at the discretion of their two MPs, Richard Norris and Sir Thomas Johnson, who appear not merely to have obtained the Act of Parliament, but also to have exercised extensive delegated powers from the Council to expedite the survey and construction. Even at this early stage, however, it is not technically correct to refer to the Common Council as the owners and managers of the Dock, for by the Act of 1709 the Council was appointed as Trustees for the Dock. The people involved were, of course, exactly the same, but the legal framework was different.

This situation led to a number of difficulties. The Council was made up of freemen of Liverpool. Its membership was governed by the Test and Corporation Acts, and the result was that the Trustees, a body which some may have felt should be analogous to the Board of a canal or private harbour company, were exclusively Anglican, predominantly Tory, and self-electing. There was no everyday mechanism by which the Trustees were accountable to port users. The ill-feeling which this situation could generate was multiplied by the right of the Council to levy Town Dues on goods passing through the port: had an unrepresentative and irresponsible body been allowed only to levy Dock Dues and Port Dues it might have aroused some discontent: when the same people wearing different hats could levy a separate set of dues with no requirement that the proceeds need in any way benefit the port, then port users were likely to get unhappy.

Unhappiness was one thing, the means of doing anything about it quite another. It was not until 1811 that any concession at all was made to the interests of the people whose money was flowing through and into the port but who had no say in its management. The Dock Act of that year created a Body Corporate, the Trustees of the Liverpool Docks. Its powers, however, were exercised by a committee made up of members of the Council in a manner not significantly different from that which had applied on an *ad hoc* basis since 1793. In the highly unlikely event of this body making any decision which was at variance with the will of the Council, its decision would inevitably fail to gain the required endorsement of 'the Trustees in Council Assembled' – a body precisely coincident with the Council.

But times were changing. The prevailing eighteenth-century nostrum 'if it disagrees with you, kill it' might still be good enough for dealing with workers at Peterloo, but was neither acceptable nor realistic when the opposition came from men of considerable intellect, wealth and commercial power. By 1823 it was clear that very serious and competent opposition was on the march, and the attempts to set the corporate house in order which had been going on since 1818 were not going to be sufficient to silence it. The mechanism which the opposition employed was the body known as the Audit Commissioners. All the Dock Acts had some audit provision built into them, but the specific provisions which were invoked were those under the 1811 Act which required the Audit Commissioners be elected each year by the users of the port. Such election was out of the control of the Council, and in 1822–3 the Audit Commissioners carried out a lengthy investigation into the building of Princes Dock.[12] In the course of this, much emerged that was corrupt even by the elastic standards of the day. The Council, so secure for so long, were faced with a very serious challenge. The Dock Act of 1825 was a masterpiece of negotiation out of a corner, in which the established majority conceded the addition to the Dock Committee of eight members elected by the dock ratepayers. These members no longer necessarily being Councillors, were not covered by the Test and Corporation Acts, so that dissenters with a stake in the port could, at last, have their say. It was a pretty limited say, however, for the remaining thirteen members of the committee had to be members of the Council, and, just as an insurance against the unforeseen, the proceedings of the committee remained subject to the veto or confirmation of the full body of Trustees. In return, the 'dissidents' had conceded the emasculation of the only body they had found capable of providing any effective opposition, namely the Audit Commissioners. The 1825 Act may look at first sight to be a move towards a wider accountability for the management of the docks: in fact it was a triumph of adaptation to preserve the powers of the Dock Trustees. Of course whether occupation of the moral high ground made for better port administration remains unproven.

It might be imagined that such an organization could not possibly survive the Municipal Reform Act of 1835. The fact of the matter is that however antediluvian its constitution might appear, the old Dock Committee had quietly cleaned up its act in the background and turned itself into a model of efficiency. It had, with more than a little prompting, dispensed with most of the jobbery and nepotism which had characterized its operation between about 1810 and 1825, and what was left in 1833, when the Municipal Commissioners made their enquiry, was a very impressive organization for its time. Even a commission of markedly Whig (some would say Radical) predisposition could find little to complain of, and most of the few

Semi-aerial view from Royal Liver Building in 1965. In the foreground the Princes Residences have just been demolished and the remains of the old South Passage filled. In the distance the west block of the corn warehouses, the east shed, West Waterloo, and the Waterloo Residences still stand

(NMGM)

complaints that were proven related to events which had occurred years ago.

The great dock building programme of the 1840s was still undertaken against a background of mercantile unrest. There were specific grievances, such as the purchase of land in Birkenhead.

The Birkenhead purchases have been much debated, appearing to some to be a cynical pre-emptive strike to prevent the development of docks on the Cheshire shore while others saw them as a costly and unprofitable speculation. What is clear is that to users of the Liverpool Docks it seemed that large amounts of money which were needed for dock improvements were being needlessly tied up in an unproductive manner. The Council also continued its policy of purchasing land which might be needed for future dock building and then reselling it to itself as the Dock Trustees, often at significant profit. Practices such as this, taken in conjunction with the long-standing grumbles over Town Dues, led to strong suspicion that the town was milking the docks and their users in a manner that was unjust and unjustifiable. The residual suspicions which had lingered on at the end of the 1833 enquiry were strengthened rather than allayed. It is not necessary at this point to consider to what extent they were justified, but merely to remark upon their existence as the background to the Dock Act of 1851, which presented considerable concessions to the mercantile and shipowning communities.

By that Act, the Dock Committee was entrusted with the entire management of the Dock Estate, and its membership was set at twenty-four, of whom half were to be elected by the dock ratepayers and half nominated by the Council. Important though this concession was, in abolishing the inbuilt Council majority, it did not alter the ownership of the docks, and neither did it have any effect on the levying of Town Dues, which now became the principal grievance. It was, therefore, only another palliative intended, like the 1825 Act, to maintain the *status quo* so far as possible.

In 1833, the prominent local firm of Bolton, Ogden & Co. had, with the support of a group of other merchants, fought a test case in which they sought to establish that the Town Dues were illegal. They lost the case, and it thus became clear that if any radical change were to occur it would be the result of background pressure and commercial arm-twisting rather than of a headlong legal challenge. A complicating factor was the trouble into which the infant port of Birkenhead had got itself through a combination of financial mismanagement and engineering misfortune. In 1855, the Liverpool Dock Trustees were forced to purchase the Birkenhead Docks, but an attempt the following year to incorporate them as part of the

Port of Liverpool was unsuccessful. Since the supporters of Birkenhead Docks, of whom the most powerful was the Great Western Railway, were significantly motivated by a desire to keep out of the clutches of Liverpool Corporation, a counter-attack was only to be expected.

'Conclaves were held in the smoke and gloom of Lancashire towns and in London',[13] and the end result was the Bill which became the 1857 Mersey Conservancy and Docks Act. The politics leading to the passage of the Act were extremely complex, but the consequences simple. The Mersey Docks and Harbour Board was established to own and manage the entire dock estate on both sides of the river. The Council was to receive from the Board the price they had paid for the Birkenhead Docks two years previously (£1,143,000) and a lump sum of £1,500,000 in commutation of Town Dues. While this latter figure represents a generous return on the sum paid to Lord Molyneux in 1672, it should be noted that the Council did not receive anything at all for the ownership of the Liverpool Docks.

The Board was to be made up of twenty-eight members, of whom twenty-four were elected by the dock ratepayers, the remaining four being nominated by the Conservancy Commissioners. It would appear that the dock users had, at last, got all they wanted in that the port was to be administered by an accountable and apolitical body whose only business was in looking after its customers and in administering an estuary which opponents of the old system likened to a great national highway. All would be sweetness and light.

All was, of course, nothing of the kind. Shipowners, merchants, manufacturers and railway companies might be capable of an uneasy cohabitation in an *ad hoc* and purely temporary alliance against a perceived common enemy like the Council, but once that enemy had been defeated the likelihood of harmonious coexistence was minimal. In theory, members of the Board were not representatives or appointees of any particular trade or interest, but in practice it would be naive to assume that they would not argue the case of their own outside interest, be it the case for investment in Birkenhead rather than Liverpool, in large docks rather than small or in warehouses rather than dry docks. The members were only human, and they could not leave their everyday working lives hanging with their top hats outside the Board Room. What was significant, however, was that the constitution of the Board, after minor alterations in 1858, proved a good and durable mechanism for the management of the port. That the Board made some misguided decisions from time to time is beyond doubt, and it was occasionally rocked by scandal, but its constitution was sound, and remained so for over a century.

CHAPTER TWO

FINGERS IN THE TILL

Ideas of Honesty

A port is rather like a bottle-neck on a river flowing with money. Goods from the broader parts funnel into the port as they are gathered for export and then disperse to the sea in a variety of directions. Similarly, imports funnel in from all over the world and are then dispersed around the country. The concentration of goods and money passing through the port has always offered opportunities to the dishonest. If the port in question had, like Liverpool in 1800, most of its business passing over open quays and through the hands of carters and warehousemen, then the opportunities were multiplied and the likelihood of detection decreased. In the presence of really heart-rending mitigating circumstances, anyone unlucky enough to be caught might be 'let off' with (fourteen years) transportation to some place the judge imagined was even nastier than Liverpool then was: normally the penalty was death.[1] Faced with such penalties, it was the minimal chance of detection which encouraged the thief. The more complicated the system, the better for the thieves.

There is a very definite reason for studying crime on the docks. Normally, the great machine of dock management rumbled on in an impersonal and complacent manner, doing things mostly as they had been done before. Because it was all so commonplace it was not recorded or, if it was, there was no need to keep the records of everyday transactions for more than a year or two. Crime changes the whole picture to a greater or lesser degree to the benefit of the historian. A simple robbery from the person may produce a decision to increase police patrols in a particular area, and to justify that expense, figures may be forthcoming illustrating the frequency or seriousness of such offences. We do not, however, learn very much. The crimes that are really informative are those which involve corruption within the system, for then we not only find people scurrying about to prove they did not do it, we also find detailed descriptions of how the system worked in order to explain how it came to be defeated. For these purposes, of course, it is not necessary for anyone to be found guilty in court: any serious degree of suspicion will suffice to set the wheels of enquiry into motion. As in the case of John Foster, the more highly placed the suspect and the more sophisticated the alleged crime, the better will be the information unearthed and retained. An allegation of corruption in the administration of justice in the docks made in 1836[2] gives us a fair idea of what a dock policeman did all day, while the Lynch case of 1903 gives a highly detailed account of the procedures for preparing and paying wages.[3]

During the period under consideration, the perception of the nature of crime changed considerably. Before about 1850 a great variety of what were dubbed by some as 'respectable crimes' were apparently not so regarded within the business community. In particular, the concept of 'hat-wearing' barely existed, so that people involved in several different ventures simultaneously saw no need to separate their own interests from those bodies corporate in which they held some position, or to separate the interests of such bodies one from another. James Brindley and George Stephenson, for example, would have been mystified at the suggestion that there was anything wrong in their using their knowledge of the future routes of canals or railways to enrich themselves by buying land along the route whose value would be enormously enhanced when the work was completed.

Two things appear to have affected this view of business ethics. The first was the growing power of the Victorian concept of the gentleman. In 1824, Everard Digby published a very curious book entitled *The Broadstone of Honour* in which he urged the adoption of the perceived values of medieval chivalry as an everyday code of life for the nineteenth century. Digby had studied Malory, and completely failed to recognize it as fiction; nevertheless, his bizarre arguments were widely read, and appear to have been influential. What is perhaps most significant about Digby is that on the subject of

The police hut (right) at Clarence Graving Docks, one of the oldest remaining. Note also the sliding gate, one of only two which survive

(Colin Pitcher)

business ethics he is silent. There were honourable landowners, squires and aristocrats, there were honourable yeomen and peasants, but there were no honourable merchants or manufacturers. Lytton's novel, *Paul Clifford*, published in 1830, went a step further by suggesting that there was no essential difference between the crimes of a highwayman and the crimes of a financial speculator. Samuel Smiles, the best-selling moralist, quoted Lytton with approbation, and described what distinguished the '*true* gentleman' and 'a *truly* noble and manly character'. His books sold by tens of thousands for

Interior view of the police hut. Robust, undoubtedly, but scarcely luxurious (Colin Pitcher)

over forty years, and since very few of them cost less than 6s 0d we may assume that the readership was predominantly middle-class. His approach, of using endless anecdotes and exemplars, conveys the impression that he is describing an existing moral consensus, but it is more likely that he was trying to create one.

The second factor was the improvement in communication, which worked in two directions. Late in the nineteenth century it was possible to claim that standards were not rising, but falling from the 'day when every gentleman's word was his bond'. When long-distance postage took several days, it was only possible to do business by trusting people to keep verbal agreements. On the other hand, the introduction of rapid railway-carried mails and of the electric telegraph made it harder to conceal any wrong-doing and the introduction of the steam printing press, resulting in the availability of cheap magazines and newspapers could render exposure widespread. As early as the 1840s, provincial newspapers like the *Leeds Times* and national publications like *The People's Journal* were willing to expose that which they considered immoral. By the 1860s, publications like the Liverpool *Porcupine* were really quite scurrilous in their coverage of business malpractice.

Many of the arguments advanced in relation to the decision-making processes of the Dock Committee and the Board require some consideration of what was or was not thought to be reasonable in terms of business ethics at the time, and these standards changed a great deal. Thus it was much 'wronger' for G.F. Lyster to allocate orders on the basis of personal patronage rather than public tender, than it was for John Foster. The best guideline for the shifting standard is to look, where possible, at responses to allegations of impropriety: a statement of current ethics is more likely to be contained in a denial, which of necessity states what is being denied, than in the accusation. An accusation may be personally motivated, it may be inaccurate or it may be based on an idiosyncratic idea of propriety: the response has to appeal to a consensus view.

It goes almost without saying that most of these values are different from those of the 1990s, although the mid-Victorian passion for competition as a stimulus to provision of better service to industry and the public has enjoyed a recent revival. When we are tempted to follow that argument, we should remember that it was almost axiomatic to the promoters of Birkenhead Docks that their competition would make for better and cheaper docking facilities on the Mersey. In the light of hindsight we can see that they were foolish and wrong, but we must be careful to recognize that their folly and wrongness lay in the assumption that they, as a bunch of beginners, could take on what was probably the most dynamic and successful port authority in the world. It did not lie in their moral views of the benefits of competition, for that is a part of their lives, and their age, which it is the historian's job to understand, not to pontificate upon.

Weighed in the Balance and Found Wanting

It is characteristic of many histories of civil engineering projects that they include great detail about the need for the project, the raising of the capital and the work of the consultant engineer. There is then a rapid leap to the festivities on opening day, leaving a great question mark over who actually did what during construction. The reason for this deficiency is not that historians have thought the subject devoid of interest, but because the information has only very occasionally survived. A Board of Directors of a canal company, for example, is mainly responsible for getting the canal built, open and earning revenue: their minutes will reflect that responsibility. Only when something goes seriously wrong will any detail show its face, and quantitatively, the thing that most often went wrong with a canal was that the engineer grossly underestimated the costs of construction. Discussion of matters technical is therefore likely to centre on heart-rending excuses for the unforeseen nature of the strata through which the summit tunnel had to be dug rather than on the exact processes used, the means of obtaining, retaining and paying the labour force, the mechanism of materials purchases, and the machinery of management control of all of these.

In theory the situation with Liverpool Docks ought to be even worse, when members of the Common Council were, technically, responsible only to the Council as a body – which meant in effect to themselves. Unlike the Board of a joint stock company there was no obligation on them to make public any minutes or accounts.[4] Although a mechanism existed for the calling of a 'Common Hall', which was the equivalent of a company's Annual General Meeting, the calling of a Common Hall occurred extremely rarely, and usually resulted in the Council continuing unperturbed upon its way.

The delegation of most of the responsibility for the Dock Estate to the Dock Committee in 1793[5] resulted in the commencement of an unusually good series of minutes of meetings which have survived as an unbroken sequence, and the first dock whose entire story, from tentative suggestion through Parliamentary powers, design and construction to opening and operation, can be traced from them is Princes Dock. Not only do the minutes go into a fair measure of detail, but also the last item on the agenda for each meeting was a

Although this view dates from as late as 1908, it still gives an impression of what dock construction was like a century earlier

(NMGM)

granting of authority to the treasurer to settle accounts, and the payments authorized are listed down to quite small amounts.

The 1811 Act was responsible for two additions to the available information. The first is perhaps only a sidelight, but none the less a revealing one, for the power granted to the committee to use two-thirds of the money raised in fines under the bye-laws for charitable purposes, resulted in the addition to the minutes of authority to the treasurer to make payments from the Charitable Fund. These not only show the Dock Committee as quite extraordinarily generous by contemporary standards (payments to a disabled man were usually about 10 shillings per week, equivalent to the full wage of a labourer) but they frequently explain why the man or his widow needed the money. We find, for example, that men were pensioned off as 'worn out and broken down' and brief details of accidents are often included, as may be the domestic circumstances of the recipient. If the risk of death or disabling accident was high, the disabled dock builder at least had the advantage that he was rarely faced with the choice between the begging bowl and parish relief.

It was Section 125 of the 1811 Act which was to make the history of Princes Dock different from that of every other municipal dock. By that section it was provided that at 12.00 noon on 25 June each year there should be elected eight Audit Commissioners responsible for examining the accounts of the Dock Committee. Although there had been audit provisions in previous Acts, this clause was of itself highly unusual. It was rendered unique by the fact that voting was not restricted to Councillors or freemen, but was open to all owners or part-owners of ships belonging to the town and also all those inhabitants 'either as principals or agents paying the rates and duties laid down under the present Act'. No other municipal enterprise in the country was open to such a widely accountable scrutiny.

The existence of such a provision would not, of itself, make for the preservation of significant historical information, for the duties of the Audit Commissioners might easily have been restricted to the examination and certification of the accounts. For them to become more extensive, two further conditions were necessary. The first was that the commissioners should not be in a position of deference towards the members of the Dock Committee, and the second was the existence of a suspicion that some part of the operations of the committee fell short of the standards of competence or honesty or both which they felt entitled to expect. Both these conditions were met, as allegations about financial improprieties at Princes Dock mounted in both number and seriousness. What made the circumstances even more interesting was that these allegations centred on John Foster Senior, the dock surveyor. He was responsible to the Dock Committee for the entire implementation of their policies, from the production of designs for structures down to the hiring and firing of the lowliest manual worker.[6] When such a man was suspected of corruption, the investigation would not be contained at the level of assorted weighing machine operators and clerks, it would go through the whole system from top to bottom. In order to consider whether or not procedures were correct or adequate it had both to describe what they were and to define what they should be.[7]

The picture which emerges is an extraordinary blend of precision and confusion. The theoretical procedure was that accounts could only be paid by the treasurer on the authority of the Dock Committee, which authority depended on the account being passed for payment by John Foster as the principal officer. He would sign only when he had received assurance from one of his senior assistants, either Leonard Addison or Henry Heyes, that the contract had been satisfactorily fulfilled. At the bottom of the reporting line came the men who weighed in materials onto the working site. Contracts would normally follow on public tendering for larger amounts or on competitive quotations from invited contractors for smaller ones. The suggestion is often made that it is unreasonable to expect modern standards of accountability, which are implied in such procedures, of an unreformed municipal borough, but the fact of the matter is that these were the standards implied by the stated procedures and born out by the survival of tradesmen's quotations for work[8] and of instructions to John Foster to advertise for tenders for the supply of, for example, stone.[9]

When a block of stone was delivered to the site, it was measured and painted with an identification mark before being either stockpiled or used. The record of its arrival, measurement and mark then passed up the accounting system. Its existence, and its progress through the site to the point where it was finally dressed and laid and appeared in the record of work made by the Measurer of Works, was all adequately recorded. Limestone, which was purchased for on-site mortar manufacture, did not lend itself to measurement, so it was gauged with one of two standard tubs, and the number of tubsfull recorded, and again passed up the system as before. Similar procedures applied to all materials arriving on site. It would appear then there was little scope for short delivery, pilferage or misuse of materials.[10]

The practice was very different. Stone for masonry work was delivered in irregular blocks from the quarry, and paid for by its usable cubic content. This entailed its being measured and an estimate then being made of the usable size when squared off. Two men were employed for this work, one for the North Works (i.e. Princes) and one for the South. Thomas Parkinson, at the South, was equipped with nothing more than 'a common rule' for undertaking this fairly complex piece of measurement, while Jonas Hogg, at the North, was stated to check stone in without the use of any instrument. If any measurement of the stone had been made at the quarry, which presumably it had, no record of it reached Hogg or Parkinson, and since both asserted that there had never been any complaint from the suppliers about their measurements, one is forced to assume that they invariably erred on the side of generosity to the supplier. It is, of course, possible that they had some incentive so to do. Had the system worked as it should, such inaccuracy or abuse should not have been long in coming to light, for the records would quickly have revealed more stone going onto the site than was accounted for in the measurement of completed work. There is no doubt that in the case of the brickwork, where bricks were easily counted onto the site, quite accurate measurement of completed work was undertaken and no significant discrepancies came to light. In the case of masonrywork, however, where the geometry could get quite complex, no measurement of completed work was ever actually undertaken.[11]

The case of the limestone was no better. Limestone was ordered and paid for by weight, but measured by volume. Depending on the size of the pieces the weight of a tubfull could obviously vary very considerably even before one takes into account the inherent confusion of measurements of weight at that time. Leaving aside the problem of the 'ton burthen' used in recording the capacity of a vessel, a 'ton' could and did vary from the modern 2,240 lbs to 2,520 lbs, and the evidence is that the people recording the weights were often uncertain as to which 'ton' was in use. Jonas Hogg, responsible for the use of the measuring tubs did not know how much they held. He believed that Mr Foster, the surveyor, knew how the weight of limestone was ascertained, but was not certain. It transpired that no one knew how much the tubs held, and their content was ascertained by practical experiment, the results of which were revealed to the Audit Commissioners on 29 October 1822. Accounts for limestone were therefore passed for payment on the basis of receipt of an unknown volume of stone which bore an unknown relationship to an uncertain unit of weight. The only clear fact which emerged was that the amount of limestone paid for was more than sufficient to sink all the boats said to have delivered it.[12]

Such problems were much less likely to occur with ironwork, as iron lends itself quite readily to weighing, and whether in the form of square bars for masonry ties or castings for buildings, the only confusion which arose was that of when a ton was a ton. In the case of

Princes Dock, nothing could be as simple as that. It may be observed that in the consideration of stone supply above, no mention is made of the quality of stone. This is because no mention is made in the contemporary documents, and it is reasonable to assume that the major repairs which were necessary to quayside and coping surfaces at a relatively early date indicate that just about any red sandstone was considered good enough and that the quality was variable. In the case of iron, and especially wrought iron, it was a very different matter.

Rather after the manner of former descriptions of egg sizes, inferior iron was designated 'best', moderately good iron was 'best best' and really good iron was 'best best best'. Adding in the uncertainties of price variations during the long period of construction of Princes Dock, a fair price for bar iron would vary between £14 and £28 per ton, depending on the quality required and the date of purchase. It was, therefore, critical to stock and budget control that the correct grade of iron was specified for the particular application, and that once it had been obtained it was identifiable in the stockyard. It is perfectly clear that no one involved in the specification, acquisition and deployment of materials had the expertise to distinguish between the different grades. It would appear from the evidence given to the Audit Commissioners that this was no unusual degree of ignorance, since a number of 'expert witnesses', all with considerable experience in the iron trade showed marked disagreement as to the quality (and hence the fair price) of a number of samples of ironwork shown to them. Much of the ironwork required was in the form of completed or partly completed components, including large quantities of very heavy bolts and nuts, and in this case subjective judgements of workmanship had to be incorporated, adding another dimension of uncertainty. The margin for error was again considerable, since a top quality blacksmith could command the very high wage of 35 shillings, while a barely adequate man would earn only about a pound. Just as in the case of the supply of bar iron, quality was crucial to price, and notions of the quality needed or received were hazy in the extreme. At its simplest, the problem was exactly the same as with stone purchases: the Dock Committee did not know what it was buying, and therefore had no idea whether or not it was paying a fair price. The indications are that it was not.[13]

Another material whose supply was open to some question was

lead. Some things change but little over a long period of time, and then, as now, lead was a favourite target for pilferers. Pilferage had a vital bearing upon the question of value for money, for the price varied widely according to the quantity purchased. It was suggested that high prices per cwt were justified by orders being placed in small lots to reduce the risk of pilferage, but equally it was alleged that any reasonable lead merchant was more than happy to take payment for a large lot and continue to store it for piecemeal issue as required. Neither this question, nor the question of exactly what constituted a ton of lead was satisfactorily resolved. The purchase of lead therefore involved two factors: the price of the metal itself and its handling or storage. The Dock Committee appears to have been completely ignorant of the second factor.

It may seem that by now more than adequate confusions have been piled upon confusion. There were, however, even further respects in which the practice of management did not accord with the theory. Although the authority of the committee was required for making payments, it was entirely open to the surveyor to enter into contracts without their knowledge or approval, and he certainly did this, especially in the case of basic materials such as wood or iron where repeated supplies were needed. Although significant sums were only supposed to be committed on the basis of public tender, the fact of the matter is that virtually no goods were so purchased.[14] The extremely contentious contract with Messrs Hetherington & Grindrod for the sole supply of stone for masonry work had been awarded in 1815 on the basis of public tender, but had been renewed on an 'old pals' basis until the time of the Audit Commission enquiry, and would, indeed, be renewed again for a further three years from 1823.[15] In virtually all other cases contracts were either handed out as a matter of municipal largesse or were awarded on the basis of restricted tendering. It is readily apparent that such contracts were likely to be awarded to relatives of members of the Council or even more likely to go to relatives of John Foster. Leonard Addison was a business partner of Messrs Hetherington & Grindrod.[16]

Thus far, the inadequacies of the management of the project detailed are largely derived from the investigations of the Audit Commissioners. There is one aspect of the work which escaped their attention, and it is one which is at least as important as those on which they enquired and deliberated at length. A quick inspection of

Groundscape at Princes. In the foreground, beach cobbles c. 1821; the middle ground shows large granite setts of, probably, 1843 and the smaller setts in the background date from the 1890s

(Colin Pitcher)

the authorizations of payments appended to the minutes of each meeting of the Dock Committee would give the impression that Princes Dock was built by contract labour. The question would then arise as to the use of the materials that Foster was ordering, which in turn would give rise to the supposition that the contracts for, for example, masonry work, were on the basis of free issue materials. This supposition may be correct, but is unfortunately unprovable, in that agreements for work which have survived do not include any of those for actual construction work.[17] We also know that there was a considerable direct labour force on the job, and that it was greatly enlarged on at least two occasions of recession by public subscriptions which provided money to employ the poor in the dock works. In the absence of any accurate measurement of work completed, the Dock Committee almost certainly knew no better than we do now what work was completed under contract and what by direct labour. If that were so, then equally they had no idea whether they had paid twice for the same work. It is, of course, highly likely that they had.

By the time construction started at Princes, nearly all of the canal network as we know it today was either under construction or completed, and it has long been accepted that these numerous large-scale works played an important part in the emergence of civil engineering as a profession in England. One aspect of this new professionalism was the evolution of some generally accepted relationships – and non-relationships. The chief engineer, commonly a famous consultant like Jessop or Rennie, was responsible for producing the overall scheme and moulding it into a form in which he could steer it through Parliament. Once he had completed this vital stage of the job he could delegate much more of the work, often reducing his own role to that of an occasional visitor. If he did this, he would have a deputy in overall charge in his absence, who would, typically, be a young man of comparable talents to his own, but of less experience. Either way, he would also appoint a resident engineer, or in the case of a canal or road of any length, several residents, each responsible for a section. For all practical purposes, the resident engineer was the boss on the working sites.

The chief advertised for contractors and would receive tenders from firms large and small. Some engineers, notably Jessop, preferred to deal with one principal contractor who would accept responsibility for the entire work, sub-contracting as necessary,[18] while others preferred to deal directly with a number of smaller firms specializing in, say, cutting and excavation, masonry, carpentry and so on. Whichever path was chosen, the result was the same, that the successful tenderer(s) worked to instructions communicated by the resident engineer. The chief was responsible to the Board or other employer for the satisfactory performance of the work, and the extent to which he delegated to a deputy or to the resident(s) was his choice, but without any effect on the line of accountability. He was, typically, paid a salary four or five times the size of that of a resident, sometimes more, and with the reward came the obligation to carry the can for everyone.[19]

At Princes Dock things worked differently. After Jessop and

Rennie had made their respective reports, they had little or no further involvement. Rennie, it is true, provided various help and advice when asked, but was in no sense the chief. John Foster effectively combined the roles of resident and chief. This was in itself a doubtful principle, for it removed the element of scrutiny by a relatively detached figure, the chief. What was far more undesirable was that, by employing direct labour on the works he was also, in effect, putting himself in the role of a contractor as well, removing the adversarial element which was fundamental to the relationship between resident and contractor. The fact that a number of suppliers were members of his family plainly did little to help.

The man to whom these considerable powers were entrusted had become dock surveyor in 1799, and it could be suggested that the departure of Thomas Morris, his predecessor, was itself his greatest feat of engineering. The son of a joiner and contractor, he had become one of the most powerful men in Liverpool, and, even in a town packed with rich parvenus, could be considered financially rather comfortable. He had no engineering training, but had performed with considerable competence in numerous large building projects and in the street and drainage improvements made under the 1785 Improvement Act. Given that there was no specific profession of Dock Engineering, and that only a handful of the great engineers like Jessop had significant achievements in the field, his experience must be considered quite acceptable, certainly good enough to qualify him to act under a 'big name' consultant such as Rennie. What he did not have was the skill to fulfill both roles, and it would be quite unreasonable to expect that he would have.

The first prominent case of a famous engineer attempting to run a project in this way was when George Stephenson attempted it with the construction of the Liverpool and Manchester Railway. He was chief engineer, and principal contractor, and also employed direct labour. Even the managerial and 'fixing' talents of George Stephenson, backed by the outstanding engineering ability of, for example, Robert Stephenson, Joseph Locke and Charles Vignoles, proved inadequate to the demands of the situation, resulting in problems of finance, ethics, engineering and logistics. The Directors had at various times to engage outside consultants to act as a check on George Stephenson, with Jesse Hartley playing an important role. Thomas has suggested that Hartley was needed for his engineering ability,[20] but it might be argued that the Stephenson team did not lack that: what it lacked was someone to fulfill the adversarial role, and it seems likely that Hartley was wanted as much for his conspicuous honesty, immovable obstinacy and noted powers of foul-mouthed vituperation as for his engineering ability. Certainly he appears to have been the only outsider who was neither ousted or worsted by George Stephenson. Even so, when Thomas Telford and his assistant James Mills examined the state of the works on behalf of the Exchequer Loans Commissioners, they found much that was inadequate or improper.[21]

If the combined talents of the Stephenson team and of outsiders of the calibre of Hartley could not avoid the problems brought about by such role confusion, what chance did the relatively inexperienced John Foster have? As we have seen, the systems for tendering and for budget and material control looked sound on paper but were almost totally ineffective in real life. To this must be added a strong suspicion that John Foster was far from possessing the very high degree of honesty required for even the most moderate success in such circumstances. His supporters have claimed that he was the municipal equivalent of an enlightened despot, bending the rules and amassing power which he then used to the benefit of the projects on which he worked. Even the most charitable view cannot deny that the building of Princes Dock took an unprecedented length of time, that when it was opened after eleven years' work it was not complete, and that it cost ten times as much per acre as had the Kings and Queens Docks, the previous two docks completed. By contrast, the West India Docks, which were nearly five times the area of Princes, were built under a conventional administration with Jessop as Chief between 1800–6. There is an element of irony in the fact that one of Jessop's residents who shared in this achievement was none other than Thomas Morris.

While those facts are damning and undeniable, they are far from inexcusable. During the whole of the period during which Princes Dock was being mooted, discussed and designed and for the first five years of its construction, Britain was at almost continual war with France. The early stages of the wars involved threat and damage to seaborne trade from enemy warships and privateers and the later stages saw the first attempt at systematic commercial warfare. As if these were not sufficient problems, the misbegotten American war of

1812 saw Britain at war with Liverpool's largest source of profit. Associated with the war came wild fluctuations in prices of basic goods and foodstuffs which in turn led to spates of financial panic and collapse. It would be hard to find a worse time at which to attempt to carry through a major project such as the building of Liverpool's largest dock to date. Other projects, such as the completion of the Leeds and Liverpool Canal, had their problems as well, and it would be quite unfair to attribute the high costs and delay of the work at Princes entirely to incompetence or dishonesty.

In one direction, Foster made a bold bid to avoid the problems brought about by war. A large part of the cost of building a dock, even one which is formed by impounding tidal water, is in the removal of spoil from a lower to a higher place. It is not only a question of getting the basin floor flat at a low enough level, but also of excavating foundations for the massive masonry of the walls and digging small tunnels for the sluices. The normal motive power for lifting the spoil was the horse, employed either on a pre-set path hauling barrows of spoil up barrow-runs or working a gin to operate a variety of types of crane or hoist. War placed an enormous strain on the supply of horses which were required in huge numbers for the transport of campaign supplies as well as for direct combat use by cavalry and artillery. The equine casualty roll of the battle of Waterloo alone has been estimated at ten thousand. At the same time food for horses, as for people, was both expensive and in short supply.

It is no coincidence that the first two milestones in steam locomotive design relate to the price of corn. Trevithick's patent of 1802 was followed by a flurry of building activity, followed by his loss of interest after 1805. The problem of rails breaking, usually given as the reason for this, may have been less significant than the fall in the price of food. Blenkinsop's patent of 1811 and the locomotives which applied it coincided with a major rise in prices, while the hiatus in development after 1815 reflects a fall. When Robert Daglish built the first locomotive in Lancashire, in 1812, he made it perfectly clear that the objective was not scientific enquiry, but the estimated saving of £500 on the cost of feeding horses.[22] It was for the same reason that William Brough, one of the contractors for the West India Docks in London, had employed a steam winding engine hauling spoil up inclines in 1805, said to have been capable of raising 2,000 tons per working day. This represents about 135 horse/hours per day for every foot depth the excavations had reached, and thus the engine allowed Mr Brough to dispense with several dozen horses if they were absolutely top-class animals, nearer a couple of hundred if they were not.

Whatever his other failings may have been, Foster was awake to this problem, and had purchased a small stationary engine from Bateman & Sherratt of Manchester for operating a winding drum to lift spoil from the workings. The exact date of its purchase is not recorded, but it was ordered to be erected at Princes Dock on 2 July 1811. It obviously exhibited more potential than achievement, for it was soon replaced by a much larger engine purchased from Boulton & Watt.[23] At a time when the use of grain for distilling spirits was forbidden and charitable subscriptions were being raised to provide cut-price grain for the poor, Foster had side-stepped the problem which was affecting the local rich as they were exhorted not to use their carriages and to feed their horses as little as possible. As soon as his steam winding system had proved its worth, he sought to improve its efficiency by laying down a rudimentary iron railway.[24] No evidence survives of where or how it was laid, and indeed it was probably altered quite frequently as work proceeded, but substantial amounts of rail were bought from the local foundry of Thomas Dove. It obviously did not entirely supplant the old system of barrowing of spoil; when the completion of the Leeds and Liverpool Canal in 1816 led to the availability of a large quantity of second-hand barrows, Foster purchased them. It is possible that in this purchase too he employed on behalf of the Dock Committee the acumen which he brought to his private dealings, for he may have foreseen that later that year he would be required to employ more hands – to the extent of five hundred men – paid for by a charitable subscription to provide work for ex-soldiers and others who were destitute as the result of the slump which followed the end of the war.

It may well be that in the contrast between Foster's acumen in these cases and his incapacity for day-to-day management we can see encapsulated the whole of the problem of Princes Dock. There was never a shortage of bold ideas, never a lack of willingness to take risks when the odds seemed right. There does not seem to be a time when it could be said that enthusiasm for the project or the determination to carry it through to a successful conclusion had waned and needed subsequently to be revived. Neither can it be said that the work was of inadequate quality, for Princes Dock is still usable today (and is occasionally used by small warships visiting the Royal Naval Reserve shore base HMS *Eaglet*). Behind the ferro-concrete staging added in the improvements of 1904–5 on the west side and of 1929 on the east, stand John Foster's red sandstone walls still in a sound structural condition. More impressive, perhaps, is the fact that his river wall not only continues to resist the powers of an occasionally violent river with only minor repair, but also survived the imposition of a heavy load of which he had no foreknowledge. For just over a century, his wall absorbed all the forces imposed by having the world's longest floating structure, the Princes Stage, attached to it, an overload which might justify the same sort of eulogy which Joseph Locke's Sankey Viaduct attracted for its ability to carry steam locomotives of the 1950s, some twenty times heavier than those envisaged when it was built.

The employment of the acknowledged management system described above did not inevitably produce results as good as those achieved by Foster: it was not a magic formula for success. Among significant failures which have come to light, two are, ironically, associated with the work of the canal contractor, John Pinkerton, for William Jessop. Pinkerton seems to have suffered from a fatal talent for underestimation, which in turn led to cash-flow problems, skimped work causing major failure of structures and head-on collision with the company employing him. What the system did provide was a mechanism for pinning down responsibility for failure, and on both the Barnsley and Dudley canals, Pinkerton ended up having to compensate the company.[25] In the case of Princes Dock the eventual quality of the work was good, but in a work which posed no special technical problems the cost and the delay were appalling. Ultimately the only control over the ambivalent position of the surveyor was that of the Audit Commissioners, a control which could be exercised only after the damage had been done. The Dock Committee learned this lesson only to a very limited extent, and was fortunate that in its next Dock Engineer, Jesse Hartley, it found a man whose integrity and managerial ability were sufficient to overcome the inbuilt problems. Once his towering presence was removed, they could recur, and they did.

From the evidence of crime and corruption we can put together a

Reconstruction of Trafalgar Dock, 1930, with portion of wall of Clarence half-tide at right mid-ground

(NMGM)

fairly accurate picture of what it was like to work on the construction of Princes Dock. There is no doubt that it was physically very demanding, for as with the building of canals all of the 'cutting' (i.e. excavation) was done by hand, only the spoil removal being to some degree mechanized. Through the questions raised over stone supply we know that part of the excavation was into rock, and that part of the workings were in fact treated as a quarry supplying stone which was re-used. No mention is made anywhere of any blasting and the likelihood is that if it had been employed there would have been complaints from owners of property very nearby, so it may be assumed that stone was cut by the traditional methods of jumper drill, wedge and feathers. The handling of stone appears to have been fairly thoroughly mechanized, as there are numerous references to cranes.

On 24 November 1813, Foster was empowered to erect a crane, to be driven from the stationary winding engine, for unloading stone delivered by boat, and on 26 August 1818 to erect a strong crane on the east side – where the wall was being built at the time. Since we know that spoil removal was largely by barrow and tramroad, these references would seem to justify the assumption that cranes were used mainly for stone. It is also clear that they were an important part of the operations, as it would not otherwise have been cost-effective to employ three watchmen and offer rewards of five pounds to prevent 'the depredations especially at the Princes Dock by persons stealing the brass bushes out of the cranes . . .' as authorized on 3 August 1819.

The work of the cutters was physically very hard, but as with the canal and railway navvies, the wages were good. Even the 'reduced wage' payable to the men taken on during the charitable work-making schemes was, at ten shillings per week, well above what an agricultural worker in the rural south could expect. No records survive of the wages normally paid to men on the direct labour force, and they certainly varied during the long period of construction, but appear generally to have been around fifteen shillings to one pound. This was, of course, ample to fund the excesses of drunken brawling, looting and rape for which railway navvies were to become notorious, but scandalized accounts of such activities by the workers at Princes Dock are conspicuous by their absence.

The size of the direct labour force fluctuated wildly according to the state of the Dock Committee's finances and the degree of urgency with which the work was being progressed. There is no doubt that at the busier stages, such as 1818, when the final push to get the dock finished had begun, there were many hundreds of men at work there. On 13 January that year, Thomas Dealy was granted the substantial ex-gratia payment of ten guineas for the extra work he had undertaken in paying the wages of the increased workforce, and a number of other junior staff were similarly generously treated. In addition to these men were the contractors' employees, notably the stonemasons of Messrs Hetherington and Grindrod working on the passage walls at both ends of the dock. There were also various small contract gangs of labourers working on spoil removal, bricklayers, carpenters and smiths from a variety of firms, but unfortunately in many cases the only evidence of the nature of their work is the extremely perfunctory description given when payment was authorized.

It is a well-known fact that until the First World War it was statistically more dangerous to be a navvy than to be a soldier, even during periods of sustained fighting. The payments from the Dock Charitable Fund provide many sidelights on the hard and dangerous nature of the work, but unfortunately do not provide us with the basis for a statistical analysis of accidents, neither do they give details of how accidents occurred. In some cases the reasons for payments are quite clear: exposure and hypothermia were a significant cause of disablement and even death during the winter of 1818 owing to the work being pushed ahead in all weathers with apparently little or nothing in the way of shelter or protective clothing for the men. Samuel Dowell, foreman of stonemasons died from this cause, as did Jonathan Grisdale, a bricklayer. Their widows were respectively awarded 'a sum not exceeding Ten Pounds' and ten shillings a week for three months.[26] Other payments require some measure of conjecture as to the exact cause of an accident. Robert Kitson, who had a wife and three children to support, was awarded forty shillings immediately and ten shillings per week for three months or until he was able to resume work. His severe injuries had been caused by his being 'thrown down from the Quay of the Princes Dock into a stone flat', but while we may reasonably assume that he had stood in the bight of the rope from the stone crane to the winding engine – a favourite way of getting thrown from a ship or quayside – there is no definite evidence to support the supposition.[27] Leg injuries were common, and while these are customarily associated with the notoriously dangerous barrow-runs used for spoil-raising, they could equally result from inept slinging of blocks of stone or large baulks of timber for craneage. John Wilson, a labourer with a wife and three children, lost a leg as a result of an accident of 16 November 1818 and subsequently died. He had been granted ten shillings per week for twelve months from the date of the accident, and after his death his widow received the same amount for a further six months from 6 September 1819.[28] It appears that need was considered as well as the nature of the injury, for John Hughes, whose leg was only broken, but who had a wife and five children to support, was awarded twelve shillings per week, while the unfortunate William Armandy, who was a single man, suffered an amputation and was awarded only the cost of a wooden spring leg.[29]

Obviously some form of accident book or similar record must have been kept to enable these committee decisions to be made, and a fascinating document it would be, had it survived. The unquantified impression of the dangerous nature of the work is, however, perfectly clear, for the committee normally met weekly and virtually every meeting passed payments similar to those mentioned above.

The Charitable Fund had other links with crime than the funds it derived from fines. A popular racket for local 'scallies' of the day was dropping bits of tackle from ships into the water, and grappling them out at a safe time for removal and sale: the committee resolved that any goods grappled from the water or recovered when a dock was drained, unless readily returnable to their rightful owner, should be sold and the proceeds added to the Charitable Fund. The system was further tightened by forbidding dock employees to have any interest in ship chandlery businesses, and forbidding ship chandlers to trade within the dock walls. Similarly when, at a later date, scavengers removing scrap wood and other materials from rubbish heaps became an inconvenience, the dock police were ordered to take steps to have useful material such as firewood scavenged officially and the proceeds again paid to the Charitable Fund.[30] On at least one occasion, the enforcement of these rules became a debit instead of a credit to the Charitable Fund, when Joseph Jones, a watchman, lost his sight as the result of a blow received while on duty and was awarded seven shillings per week.[31]

At the time of the construction of Princes Dock there was no legal responsibility on an employer to take any precautions whatever for the safety of his workers, nor to pay any compensation or disability pension in the event of an accident. The Dock Committee was an outstandingly generous employer in this respect, and while it is true that for much of the time they could well afford to be, it is only fair to remark that in many an unreformed incorporated borough the product of bye-law fines was more likely to be spent on some distinguished additions to the Town Hall wine cellar than on mitigating the effects of industrial accidents. In private industry, compensation or relief of this kind was exceedingly rare. In writing, therefore, of the provisions made for the direct labour force, one omits any mention of those who had the worst of the job: the employees of small contractors and the self-employed. These men worked in conditions at least as dangerous and arduous as did the Corporation's men without the protection from destitution afforded by the Charitable Fund, and in the case of the self-employed, payment by the cubic yard of spoil or other measurement of work done could add a dangerous component of additional haste to the risks already run in the normal course of events. Neither should it be forgotten that first aid for any serious accident more or less began and ended with the saw and the bucket of hot pitch: not only were the chances of accidents high, but the likelihood of an accident leading to permanent disability, and therefore destitution, was high. There was no legal right to any form of compensation. It must have been only a slight consolation that Liverpool was an extremely rich and charitable town, equipped with a poor-house of far above average quality, capable of holding up to 1,500 paupers and having in addition a substantial budget for outdoor relief. In 1819 the cost of these provisions amounted respectively to £13,453 and £20,050.

Princes Dock survived almost unaltered until 1904, but has since been so heavily altered that it is difficult to gain any feeling of what it used to be like. The walls of the half-tide dock, large parts of which appear to be the originals although they were in fact rebuilt in 1868, give a better impression of the bulk and quality of the masonry work and of the blood and sweat which went into building a dock. We can remember that it was built by large numbers of men, but everyone an individual, some honest, some corrupt, some clever, some stupid.

The masonry to the right is part of John Foster's work on Princes Basin, as relaid by G.F. Lyster in c. 1866

(Colin Pitcher)

Some of them enjoyed high wages and the benefits of working for a generous employer, others ended their employment there on parish relief or in a pauper's grave. Was it one of those stones we see which fell on John Wilson's leg? Where had Robert Kitson been standing when he was thrown down from the quay? These men have no biographies except the stones they left behind them, which remain, as they were described on the opening day, 'a magnificent monument'.

LIVERPOOL CENTRAL DOCKS

Revelations of a Victorian Whistleblower

The Mersey Docks and Harbour Board was established with a view to its being a body which was disinterested in anything other than the efficient operation of the port. Its members were to be elected or nominated with that end in view, and it is probably fair to say that great hopes were held for the future of this new body, which seemed to promise an altogether fairer and more democratic way of managing the docks than had the old system of effective control by the Liverpool Council.

The old system had not necessarily been all that bad. It had, on paper at least, a measure of public accountability which was initially unique and which remained unusual. It had employed an engineer of outstanding ability and integrity and had succeeded in keeping itself well ahead of competing ports. The failing which had led to the campaign for a more broadly accountable body was that it had not convinced its customers that it had interests wider than the well-being of Liverpool at heart. It may well be that criticisms on these grounds were ill-founded, but what mattered was the perception of the Dock Trustees and, whatever the realities might have been, they were perceived as being dominated by parochial Liverpool interests.[32]

The inauguration of the new Board was, therefore, greeted with a fair amount of enthusiasm as heralding a new stage in the development of a port whose growth under the old system had been prodigious. The hopes were for even greater benefits in the future, but they were hopes which were to prove sadly misplaced. Although the tonnage of shipping using the port continued to increase dramatically, the rate of increase had already turned down by the time the Board was established, and it continued to decline throughout the period of this book. Because these seeds of decline were masked by the rising total figures, little action was taken to turn round the fortunes of the port: it is quite clear that most Board members simply did not recognize the indications of a need for change.

The Central Docks were, by this time, almost entirely useless for the purpose for which they had been built. Their narrow entrance passages, barely wide enough for a present-day ferry boat,[33] were outgrown by the width of ships in use on the North Atlantic, with the result that they had come mainly to handle traffic from those ocean trades which used relatively small vessels, particularly those of the

Fig. 2 Hartley-style roof trusses of 1843, Princes Dock north-west shed

East and West Indies with varying degrees of adequacy. Jesse Hartley had correctly determined that the new docks needed for larger vessels would be better built further down river, and no significant modernization of the Central Docks took place during his tenure of office. Following the brief 'reign' of J.B. Hartley, terminated in 1861 by his retirement through ill-health, George Fosberry Lyster was appointed as engineer, and held the post until 1897. Early in his long period of office, he was responsible for the complete reworking of Waterloo Dock and the access to it via Princes Basin.[34] The basin, which had originally been fully tidal and of little use except as an entrance to Princes and Waterloo Docks, was entirely changed in shape and provided with a magnificently constructed triple entrance closely resembling that at Salisbury Dock – so closely resembling it in fact that it is often erroneously assumed that it is the work of Jesse Hartley. Waterloo Dock, formerly a rectangular basin with its shorter side to the river, was divided into two, West Waterloo providing berths for medium to small sized ocean-going vessels and East Waterloo becoming a specialized grain dock with the latest and best facilities for handling bulk grain. These improvements, completed in 1868, were extremely durable: the new Princes half-tide dock remained in traffic until the 1960s and the surviving east block of the Waterloo Corn Warehouses was still handling oil seeds in 1987.

The brief narrative above could be taken as evidence of an awareness of the problems of obsolescence in the Central Docks, and a determination to apply a high standard of engineering expertise to their solution. The work of both Mountfield and Hyde would reinforce such an impression, and the reason for this slightly rosy picture is that the career of G.F. Lyster exhibits a considerable recrudescence of the problems brought about by the lack of any form of adversarial engineering management which had occurred so markedly under John Foster. At a superficial level, the Board was well pleased with the activities of the Engineer's Department, with the result that only good news emerged.

Beneath the surface, the picture is rather different. There was an adversary on the Board, and much of the evidence he unearthed indicates that the Engineer's Department was not at all well managed. Harold Littledale was a successful cotton merchant who was one of the original nominee members of the Board, and appears to have taken little or no interest in engineering matters until his election to the Works Committee in 1872. Almost at once, he began to question the way things were done in the Engineer's Department, and although he was almost invariably voted down by other members, the issues he raised, and the information which he brought forth in raising them, were matters of vital importance to the operation of the docks. While he may not have been right in every case, it is certainly true to say he was right more often than he was wrong, and that in every case where he was right he drew attention to significant examples of incompetence or malpractice. His allegations, therefore, have the same benefits for the historian as the allegations against John Foster, of bringing forth evidence which would otherwise have remained hidden.

The first issue in which he became heavily involved was that of competitive tendering, with particular reference to the supply of hydraulic machinery by Sir W.G. Armstrong & Co. Very few public bodies in the mid-1870s awarded contracts of any significance without seeking tenders, and the unreformed Dock Committee had ordered as long ago as 1824 that goods should be purchased in that way.[35] Littledale not only discovered that Armstrong's were invariably invited simply to make an 'offer to supply' but was also met with the astonishing assertion by the engineer that he wished he were allowed to seek competitive tenders and to present them to the committee, as it would remove a great weight from his shoulders.[36] Further enquiries revealed that it was the exception rather than the rule for tenders to be sought in any situation where there was a customary supplier. This was a long-standing breach both of contemporary business practice in public bodies and of the traditional procedures on the Liverpool Docks, yet when Littledale asked the Board to refer back one of Armstrong's offers with a view to obtaining competitive tenders, he was voted down 22–2.[37] The majority of the Board simply did not want the boat rocked. Littledale went on to discover other malpractices within what he frequently referred to as 'a vicious system', some of which might give rise to suspicion of corruption on the part of G.F. Lyster. One such was the appointment of junior engineers on the staff who were not paid a salary, as they should have been, but a weekly wage. This meant that the posts were Lyster's exclusive gift, without reference to the Works Committee or the Board. Of fourteen pupils who paid fees to Lyster between 1861 and 1881, ten were later employed in this manner, one of them being Lyster's own son. When the Works Committee was prodded into making some enquiry as to the expenditure on weekly paid employees they were told and at first accepted, that no statement of the weekly wages existed.[38] It is equally hard to imagine that a department with an annual expenditure approaching seven digits had no record of its employees or their wages, or that any member of a Board Committee could be sufficiently gullible to believe that such could be the case. The effrontery of Lyster in attempting to conceal his patronage in this way is astonishing, and gives a clear indication of his estimate of the astuteness of the committee. The minute detail recorded in the surviving Total Cost of Works ledgers shows that this was a deliberate lie.

It could be suggested that there really was no need for Lyster to behave otherwise: tendering, for example, does not necessarily result in the best and cheapest deal for the customer and it could certainly be argued that public advertisement is not the most efficient way of appointing staff. But Lyster did not argue either of these points: when accused of using orders and appointments as a form of patronage he resorted to lies and to the invocation of invalid precedents from the days of Hartley. These devices constitute an admission that what he was doing was not consistent with good business practice or ethics of the period.

Lyster appears to have resembled John Foster, in that his acumen was sharper in his own dealings than in his dealings on behalf of the Board. In 1882, John Jones, a clerk in Lyster's department, was gaoled for his involvement in a fiddle relating to the supply of gravel for use as aggregate in concrete in the new South Works. The principle of the fraud was extremely simple: John Beckett, the contractor, invoiced the Board for far more gravel than had actually been delivered and John Jones certified these fraudulent bills as correct. The proceeds were then divided. This will be readily recognized as a reincarnation of the Princes Dock Stone Fiddle, and, by a curious coincidence, it proceeded for the same length of time before detection and when it was detected, it was detected by the same means. Beckett, like his over-ambitious predecessors, had paid Dock Dues not on the amount he claimed to have delivered, but only on the amount he actually had delivered. If it might appear that the Engineer's Department had an inadequate control of their materials, allowing them to be taken for a ride in such a time-honoured manner, it should be added that their incompetence was compounded when they were asked to quantify the loss. The sums mentioned in the prosecution of Jones and Beckett totalled £19 9s 6d, while the estimate given to the Works Committee was £250 and the sum claimed in the civil suit following the prosecution was £6,186.[39] Was the loss in two, three or four digits? Or more, or less? Who knew? Littledale hinted darkly that there was more to emerge in this case, clearly implying that he had reason to believe that persons more highly placed than John Jones were party to it. If he did have valid grounds for suspicion, he never succeeded in finding proof, and the matter was dropped. It had, however, proved that the Engineer's Department was run in a sloppy manner. What is perhaps more significant is that at no stage did the Works Committee attempt to make Lyster, who was paid the very substantial salary of £4,500 to carry the can for his department, accept any measure of responsibility for this failure of his system. They trusted their engineer, and they distrusted the elderly trouble-maker who kept attacking him. Had they been a little wiser, they might have questioned what Littledale stood to gain from his attacks and realized that the answer was nothing, except for being part of an organization which was no longer governed by 'a vicious system'.

The vagueness of a system which allowed a couple of petty thieves to get away with an insignificant amount of money may seem to be of little importance. It is, of course, no more than an indicator of how the system worked, but the working of that system was close to being a matter of life and death for the Board. The Engineer's Department spent over one eighth of Board revenue on routine works, and by far the greatest part of the Board's capital on major improvement schemes. It was a very large business, and the accuracy of its estimating and the quality of its financial performance depended, in the end, on accurate stock and budget control. In this and several other incidents, notably the Lynch case, below, it was shown that however copious the paperwork might be, the results were poor.

The application of this inefficiency to the problems of the Central Docks is not immediately apparent, yet is always present in the background. The administrative inefficiency shown in the case of Jones and Beckett combined with the desire of Board members to keep the boat on an even keel became extremely harmful when added to the third ingredient, engineering errors. As a rough generalization, it is probably fair to say that no major construction or reconstruction scheme undertaken during Lyster's tenure of office was free of serious error. His completion of the Great Low Water Basin in Birkenhead was a disaster,[40] his extension of the Floating Stage an incompetence in the face of correct expert advice thirty years before.[41] His design for the Morpeth Warehouses was untenable[42] and his successive reworkings of Canada entrance can only be described as sheer bumbledom. In each of these cases, Littledale drew attention to what was happening, and in each case events proved him right. Perhaps one example should be cited in more detail to provide some support for such contentious suggestions.

In 1873, an Act was obtained for the largest and most expensive extension yet made to the Dock Estate. One component of it was the Langton Graving Docks, which were to be constructed to accommodate the largest North Atlantic vessels. When questioned in Parliamentary Committee on the dimensions and construction of these graving docks, Lyster's response was 'Having eighteen graving docks at Liverpool, I am able to say the best form to adopt, and I have designed them accordingly'.[43] This would seem to be the statement of a man adequately sure of his own expertise, yet by 1888, just nine years after the new graving docks were completed, it was public knowledge that they were of inadequate size for exactly the type of vessel for which they had supposedly been designed.[44] In the meantime, the Canada entrance, which was part of the same programme, had been deepened by a further three feet at an estimated additional cost of £200,000, a sum which later grew to £460,000. The failure to design and construct new docks at enormous expense in such a way as to meet their most basic design parameter even after ongoing design changes at considerable additional expense, cannot be regarded as the work of an engineer deserving of portrayal as a worthy successor to Jesse Hartley. The effects on the Central Docks of these failures elsewhere were serious, though perhaps not as serious as those of the determination of the Board to convince itself that all was for the best in this best of all possible ports.

All in all, however, consequences for the Central Docks were dire. Problems in the huge expansion and modernization programmes proceeding both to the north and the south resulted in a shortage both of money and of design time. The works under the 1873 Act proved to be a resource-guzzler whose effects extended directly until the mid-eighties, and indirectly (via the interest charges on their excess expenditure and the correction of errors) for much longer. It may be stretching the argument over-far to suggest that it was a result of the problems on those works that the final stage of the modernization of Princes Dock had to wait until 1928 when the sale of the Clarence Dock site for a Liverpool Corporation Power Station provided the funds. It would appear, however, that the 1904–5 improvements in the Central Docks were severely curtailed by lack of funds and it should be remembered that they were in their turn the first major improvements since 1868. In December 1958 the Docks & Quays Committee took the decision to demolish a shed on the east side of Nelson Dock: it was the original open shed of 1849 with the sides infilled.

More serious still were the continuing effects of the inadequacy of

A set of impounding pumps, probably those at Sandon. These gargantuan machines delivered over 38,000 gallons per minute each, *and were installed to paper over the problems of insufficient depth in the new North Works*

(NMGM)

the design of the North Works under the 1873 Act. This, the largest capital programme the docks had seen, fell so far short of what was needed that Mr Glynn, Chairman of the Works Committee, could say to the Board, on 2 June 1892, that the work 'when the mortar as you may say was hardly cold was found to be entirely insufficient for the trade'. The result was a programme of corrective works of enormous extent and cost. The initial estimate, made public in July 1890, was for £530,000, and the arguments presented in favour of proceeding are a severe indictment of what had gone on only ten years before.[45] There were, for example, only 116 days of the year when a vessel of the unexceptional draught of 26 ft could enter or leave Liverpool Docks. The sill of the Canada entrance, specifically intended for the largest ships, was a mere six feet below that of the Old Dock of 1715 and three feet above that of the modest Old Dock at Garston. The Board had agreed to lower the sill to 18 ft 6 in below ODS on 21 February 1890, to 20 ft below on 23 May and on 27 April 1894 by a further six inches. In each case, of course, additional cost was involved.

The new Langton Graving Docks had proved so inadequate that it was necessary to construct a new 'state of the art' dock at Sandon. This was designed to be 650 ft long, then 710 ft, then 750 ft and finally, on 22 February 1895, 810 ft. Each minute approving alterations also approves increased cost, and each is marked 'Not to be read in the presence of the reporters'. Behind these changes lay the changing interests of members, as well as engineering indecisions, and the interactions of the two deserves further investigation.

With the indecision went the delay. In December 1892 the Chairman of the Board stated that a year previously he had said that 'by this time' the important alterations at Canada would be within measurable distance of completion. He now accepted that re-opening would be delayed until 'early 1894', but in fact that entrance did not re-open until August 1895.[46] The ways in which such delays occurred are catalogued in the tale of woe attached to the writ in which Messrs Eckersley & Co., contractors for the excavation of Canada Branch Dock, claimed compensation from the Board for losses incurred. The document is a lengthy one, but the grounds of the claim may be summarized: the Board caused endless delay in those parts of the works which were their responsibility, had misled the contractors as to the nature of the work, provided insufficient pumping capacity, caused physical obstructions to the site, changed their minds about where spoil was to be tipped, changed their minds about the methods of working and caused numerous inundations of the site by inept treatment of drains and culverts, as well as one major incident when a dam burst. The list of wasted man/days and of heavy plant, such as steam navvies and locomotives, standing idle is revealing.[47]

The Board was perfectly well aware that the Central Docks were in dire need of modernization, and a scheme for thoroughgoing improvements from Salisbury as far south as Waterloo was presented to the Works Committee in November 1889. The needs may be briefly stated: the most recent of these docks had been completed in 1848 and only Waterloo and Princes half-tide had been modernized to any significant degree. At all the other docks, the sheds were with few exceptions small, dark and devoid of any mechanical handling equipment. The passage and entrance gates and the movable bridges were without exception hand-operated. Some of the quay walls had a batter of several feet, acceptable with fairly round-bilged sailing vessels but a positive hazard to deeper and squarer-bilged steamers. The passage to Princes Dock had such large 'haunches' that it was possible for a steamer to ground heavily on both bilges while having feet to spare at water level and, indeed, under its keel. Except at Waterloo, not one of these docks had changed to take account of the fact that, given proper facilities, a steamer could discharge at a minimum of three times the rate of a sailing vessel of similar size. All this was well known to members, some of whom were involved in the operation of relatively small ships and all of whom had some direct financial interest in the efficient working of the port.

Further discussions occurred at a number of meetings in 1889 and 1890, until 21 February 1890 when it was 'Resolved (Mr Holt dissenting): that the projects for the improvement of the docks between the Nelson and the Waterloo Docks be not entertained'. In 1885, a categorical promise had been given that no major new works would be undertaken until the problem of the Central Docks had been resolved, with a view to providing excellent specialized facilities for the coastwise trade.[48] Even this promise, belated as it was, was not entirely honoured, for the 1898 Act under which improvements were at last made, was also concerned with yet further major works at Canada and Huskisson Docks and with large-scale remodelling of Kings and Queens Docks.

The works of 1904–5, coupled with a number of minor improvements in the interim, at last turned Princes Dock back into a useful asset, offering first-class facilities for coasters, and good, modern sheds were available there and, for example, at Nelson, Trafalgar and West Waterloo. Even so, the old East Princes shed survived, as did East Nelson and all the Clarence sheds. No improvements were made to the river entrances, neither were the passages widened. Rail access was considerably improved as part of A.G. Lyster's widespread reversal of his father's marked antipathy towards rail haulage on the docks. In fairness it must be stated that, although the 1904–5 and 1928 programmes were undoubtedly too late, and possibly too little, they proved highly successful. The final demise of these docks probably has more to do with the inability of the coasting trade to compete with the sustained and deliberate onslaught launched by the railway industry, with the losses sustained in two world wars and with the speed and flexibility of the motor lorry.

The long sequence of controversies in which Harold Littledale was involved almost until his death in 1889 had the customary effect of accusations of corruption or incompetence, namely a great improvement in record-keeping. It also had the perhaps less customary effect of bringing about a rather more open forum among the members of the Board which seems gradually to have moved towards members being better informed and hence making more effective decisions. After Littledale's retirement from the role of whistleblower, Alfred Holt was briefly but effectively antagonistic with similar results. Holt's particular interest was in the adequate provision of up-to-date facilities for medium to small-sized vessels, and had he not felt it necessary to resign in 1892 it is possible that improvements in the Central Docks would have come sooner and been more extensive. While, with the benefit of hindsight, it is possible to say that Holt probably showed insufficient foresight in his opposition to the provision of facilities for large and ever-growing ships, it is also possible to see that his opponents were spending money on schemes which, although large and expensive, were not tackling the problem of access for large vessels at its root.[49]

In 1903, the Institute of Public Health held its conference in Liverpool, and those attending were provided with a publication describing the city to which they had come. It is, in fact, a substantial book providing an excellent record of many aspects of Liverpool at the time. Among its contents is an account of the docks, written by Miles K. Burton, the General Manager and Secretary to MDHB. In this, it is not as one might expect, the most recent and northerly docks, namely Langton, Alexandra and Hornby which are described as providing the best accommodation for the largest vessels. The finest accommodation is, we are told, in the Canada Huskisson system – docks built by Jesse Hartley in the 1850s and improved by A.G. Lyster since the retirement of his father. Even more striking is the statement that the entrance for those same docks is not the Canada entrance on which such huge resources had been expended, but A.G. Lyster's 1901 remodelling of Jesse Hartley's smaller and earlier entrance at Sandon. The Gladstone entrance, opened in 1911 was the final solution in the sense that it handles the largest container ships and bulk-carriers of the present day, but the Canada entrance problem was not really solved until the tidal basin was done away with completely and the present Langton Lock opened – in 1961.

By the turn of the century, the Board had been established long enough for many of its ordinary day-to-day procedures to have become features of an ossified bureaucracy. Such systems are obviously wasteful in themselves for a variety of reasons, including the extremely low level of motivation for clerical staff at all grades. Any perceived defect in the system is likely to be remedied only by the addition of further complications, with a resulting rise in overheads. These difficulties were not critical in the case of docks built for very large vessels, because the limited number of such docks nationwide all suffered the same problem.[50] The case of docks for smaller vessels was quite different, in that vessels of up to a couple of thousand tons had a fair measure of choice of port even within the Mersey, and the Central Docks had to compete with such small ports as Garston, Runcorn, Weston Point and Ellesmere Port.

The opening of the Manchester Ship Canal in 1894 not only introduced an entirely new competitor, but also enabled large vessels to reach the last three named small ports much more easily. None of these competitors was burdened with the overheads of inefficient and outdated facilities of great extent, nor with the excess administrative costs mentioned above.

Normally, the system ground along with a ponderous inevitability. It worked just well enough that no one troubled to make a top-to-bottom enquiry even of how it worked, much less how well it worked. The historian, therefore, owes a considerable debt of gratitude to a certain John Lynch, timekeeper in the Engineer's Department.

Mr Lynch was observed to enjoy a style of living which was not commensurate with his wages. This was well known among his colleagues and his fellow timekeeper John Banfield gave evidence that:

> There was talk in the Dockyard about the way Lynch was living. The general talk was that he had a private income; that he was reared to be a priest, that he could speak French; and that he had to work in Liverpool only or he could not receive this private income.[51]

Lynch, in his confession, stated quite clearly that he lived in an elegant house in Ivanhoe Road, off Sefton Park, at an annual cost of £55, that he kept two servants, that he smoked several 18d cigars per night and had a particular liking for 'Pomeray', a wine which, at 13s per bottle was more the style of a chief engineer than of a timekeeper.[52] He was paying over £12 per month for furniture on hire-purchase (that alone exceeded his total legitimate wages) and had about another £7 per week in general household expenses. He spent freely on drink for his friends and appears to have been a 'sugar daddy' to a number of younger women (at least two of whom thanked him by blackmailing him) while, at the same time, doing the relatively decent thing by his wife through investing money in trust for her.

The truth of the matter was, of course, that Lynch did not have a private income, neither had he been lucky on the horses. He was working the 'fictitious employees' racket on a large scale and with singular success. The total number of names involved was over fifty, and Lynch admitted to using up to thirty-four at one time. (The prosecution alleged forty-one.) The total amount of money involved in a period of some eighteen months was well over £3,000. Lynch and his accomplice, Rous, both pleaded guilty and received prison sentences whose brevity in relation to the seriousness of the offences must indicate that they were a likeable pair of rogues who gained sympathy from the court: what is significant in terms of the history of the Dock Estate is the detail of how the pay system in the Engineer's Department worked – or did not work – much of which did not come

Men of the Engineer's Department collecting their wages. This photograph was taken to be produced as evidence in the Lynch case

(NMGM)

out in court, but which is contained in statements made by Lynch before the trial.

The failures of an extremely complicated system began with the travelling timekeepers of whom Lynch was one. They were meant to visit each location where manual employees of the Engineer's Department were working, twice a day, and record their hours worked in a notebook. Since many of the men involved worked aboard floating plant and timekeepers could not walk on water, this was plainly impractical, with the result that a certain proportion of the contents of timekeepers' pocket-books was pure fiction. Because the job was impossible to do correctly, many timekeepers, Lynch among them, simply did not bother even to try. The next stage was that when the pocket-books went into the office to be translated into a time-sheet, there were commonly manifest errors, which were simply altered in such a way as to make sense of them. When it is considered that just one trade, millwrighting, working on just one category of job, repairs to dredging plant, accounted for an average of fifty men, the scale of the problem becomes clear. Time-sheets too were commonly altered, as Lynch's statement made clear 'I was not aware that I was committing forgery in altering these sheets: it was a common thing to be done'. It was also clear that alterations needed no reference to higher authority. The irregularities continued right through to the point where a workman, having received his pay ticket, went to a pay hut to cash it in. Again the floating plant men were the main problem, turning up to collect their pay at peculiar hours, and the accepted practice was for them to go to the side door of the pay hut which 'was of course, contrary to the rules, but then the whole system of pay at the dredging was irregular'. It opened the way for various abuses, one of which Lynch exploited.

Three different offices in two different buildings were involved, and Lynch stated that 'I carried out the frauds practically single-handed with no other help but the looseness of the system and the amazing neglect, remissness and carelessness of the officials in the three departments of the Board; the Time Office, the Wages Bill Department and the Check Office.' Of the Check Office, he claimed that 'they were all groggy in both senses of the word. I have paid men myself late on a Saturday night. Thorpe was one of the boozy men . . . Thorpe came down speechless one night and told the men to help themselves . . . If I had kept sober I could have made £150 a week or over in the dredging.' Most of these allegations did not form part of his formal deposition, presumably because his lawyer advised him that they would not help him, and all of them were denied by the Board, though not to the extreme of claiming that none of the pay clerks was ever drunk, merely that when they were they still did not make mistakes.

It could be that in making these accusations, Lynch was protecting one or more further accomplices who had not been detected, claiming that the system was so bad that anyone could perpetrate serious fraud with some ease. The strongest piece of evidence to suggest that Lynch was speaking the truth is perhaps the fact that the Board, in preparing to describe to the court how the wage system worked found it necessary to take fifty-two statements from potential witnesses and formal depositions from twenty-seven individuals. Yet it was also true that several unwitting accomplices of Lynch had, on different occasions, succeeded in collecting several pay packets each, sometimes disguising themselves by such subtle means as wearing a different form of headgear. When Lynch went on holiday for two weeks he solved his problem by booking leave for thirty-four friends to go at the same time: no work ground to a halt as a result, for the obvious reason that the thirty-four friends did not exist – and nobody noticed. It is also worthy of note that these frauds began when a bona fide error remained undetected.

The Lynch case illustrates the detail administration of the largest department of the Board with some clarity, and what is shown is a body whose administrative system had grown haphazardly to the point where it was of mind-bending complexity and was yet incapable of meeting the rudimentary needs for which it was devised, namely paying employees the money they were due at the right time and in such a way as to keep accurate records of who had been paid how much for what work. In the process, its lower and middle managerial staff had been totally demoralized by having to operate a system which contained manifest absurdities and which could only be made to function by routine breaches of the rules. It appears that this had the predictable effect of causing good and conscientious staff to leave, so that the remainder contained a significant proportion of the breathtakingly stupid and the habitually drunk. Burdened with such a system, it was highly improbable that the Engineer's Department could produce accurate estimates for proposed new work, control its budget during the process of the work or even determine the correct cost after the work had been completed. Even in such a large establishment, the inability evident in the holiday episode to schedule work to within a margin of plus or minus sixty-eight man/weeks must be considered a serious weakness. In the broader picture, it seems obvious that it was this failure of costing and scheduling which had led to the problems faced by the unfortunate Mr Eckersley, and to the delay and overspending on the alterations to the Canada entrance. We should not be surprised that humble projects like the improvement of the Central Docks, which came well down on the list of priorities, had to wait a long time, and that when they eventually did receive attention they were burdened with overheads which were not only higher than the trade could readily bear, but which were absent in smaller and newer competing ports. Seen against that background, the apparently dilatory improvements of 1904–5 were surprisingly effective and may even be an early indication that the administrative shambles which characterized the Engineer's Department in the latter quarter of the century was at last on its way to being sorted out.

The Landscape of Dishonesty

There is some measure of doubt as to what shades of dishonesty were tolerable in nineteenth-century business practice, and it may be for example, that when Dickens excoriated the manipulators of railway capital, he was just a voice crying in a wilderness where such things were normal practice. Similarly there were undoubted differences of opinions as to the degree of personal risk at which one might legitimately place employees. On one issue, however, it appears that there was some measure of unanimity: for centuries the cheating of HM Customs (and/or Excise) was the moral equivalent of parking on a single yellow line five minutes earlier than allowed. It was a crime with no visible victim, and one which could produce large gain at small risk. On some traditional Liverpool cargoes, notably North American tobacco and West Indian rum, the duty commonly exceeded the value of the goods, which had provided a compelling incentive to dishonesty since the seventeenth century.

An equally powerful incentive was the mind-boggling complexity of the calculation of duty, with up to thirteen different duties to be calculated and paid on a single item of cargo.[53] These calculations would test a beginner even today, armed with a personal computer, and were quite incomprehensible to the average late eighteenth-century shipowner or merchant. The eminently practical solution was that merchants paid fees to the Customs officers to do this work for them, and by the beginning of our period this happy bit of *ad hocery* had evolved to the point where the officers' salaries were a fairly insignificant part of their income. Scope for corruption was not lacking.

Many are the exciting yarns of late eighteenth-century Customs men involved in violent clashes with armed gangs of smugglers. So great were the rewards of smuggling that some gangs even fitted out what amounted to small warships to defend their ill-gotten gains. But this was not, in the main, the Liverpool way: Liverpool criminals seem to have preferred corruption and subterfuge to force. There is, however, a basic historical problem in dealing with their activities, because all such methods of fraud depend on one simple principle, the concealment of the existence of goods liable to duty. The exact method might vary – the two main variants were the concealment of the goods altogether and the falsification of their nature or origin – but the principle employed means that a successful Customs evasion leaves no evidence for the historian. The only exception to this rule is where some other evidence quite separate from the fraud itself exists as in the case of the activities of Sir Thomas Johnson at the very beginning of the eighteenth century, some of which can be pieced together from surviving documents in the Norris Papers.[54]

Nevertheless, there is a valid reason for considering Customs offences even though exact evidence of their nature and occurrence is slender, and that is the profound effect which countermeasures had on the built environment of the Central Docks.

In 1799, nearly all goods arriving in the port were discharged onto open quays around the docks, where they were examined by Customs, duty was paid on them where required and they were then consigned to some or other of the large number of small warehouses spread round the lower part of the town. The quays had little or no physical separation from the streets of the town,[55] and there was, thus, a serious likelihood of various forms of fraud occurring between landing and payment of duty. Old favourites included the abstraction of fairly small quantities of liquid or absorbent goods and the replacement of the weight with water. As long as the goods were duty paid, there was not a great deal for Customs to worry about. There were, however, moves afoot to adopt the system of bonded warehouses, in which goods could be stored duty free until they were withdrawn for resale or use. This would have the benefit of removing the complications of the old 'drawback' system from which many a Liverpool merchant had dishonestly profited, but it made physical security on the quaysides very much more important.

A late eighteenth-century transit shed was nothing like the building which is nowadays called to mind by that expression; far from being virtually a single-storey warehouse, it consisted of a roof on stilts. Its only function was to keep the rain off goods during sorting or examination. Some sheds were equipped with provision for rigging sail-cloth sidescreens, while truly luxurious ones had one or more sides enclosed with weatherboarding, to keep out the horizontal rain which often occurs on the Liverpool waterfront. Neither gave the slightest protection against theft, and the more enclosed ones could make examination pretty difficult: glass being both expensive and available only in small sizes, skylighting was minimal so that their interiors were gloomy in the extreme. When, therefore, Liverpool became a warehousing port, in 1805, it was to be expected that there would be pressure for improvements in security.[56]

One method was to build warehouses on the Dock Estate itself, and in 1799 the Kings Dock Tobacco Warehouse was among the largest buildings in the town. This, partly anticipating the bond system, was a Crown warehouse in which tobacco was stored duty free, and the hogsheads of tobacco were rolled into it immediately on landing, all weighing and examination being carried on inside. This method had such obvious attractions, not only in terms of preventing fraud, but also in simplicity of handling goods that it is, at first sight, surprising that Liverpool's new status as of 1805 did not immediately lead to a spate of warehouse building on the Dock Estate. In fact, the next few years saw only one significant dockside warehouse erected, which was the new Kings Dock Tobacco Warehouse, an enormous building for its time, with a floor area of over three acres. The only substantial warehouses already existing which were immediately adjacent to a quayside (with the exception of the Duke of Bridgewater's warehouses on his privately owned dock) were the Goree Warehouses, completed in 1793 to the east of Georges Dock.

There were two main reasons why warehouses did not proliferate along the quaysides. The first was the fear of fire. Both ships and warehouses of the time burned very well, as did many of their contents, such as rum, tobacco and sugar. The likelihood was that if they were in close proximity, a fire in the one would ignite the other. A major warehouse fire would almost invariably cause the complete collapse of the structure, resulting in severe danger to life as well as property. The financial losses could be catastrophic: the Goree Warehouse fire of 1802 did damage estimated at £323,000.[57] This can be put in context by recalling that ten shillings a week was a fair wage for an unskilled man or that £500 p.a. was a decidedly large salary. It was remarked at the time that it was most fortunate that the wind was onshore, as otherwise the ships in Georges Dock would have caught fire before they could be removed to a safe distance, resulting in far greater destruction even than that which occurred. The few hand-operated fire pumps then available were more effective than one might expect from looking at preserved examples, but were still quite helpless in the face of a major warehouse fire: the Goree fire would have been quite a test for modern appliances. The major problem was the roof: in the absence of access equipment the firefighters could only get water into the upper part of the building by pumping a jet to the roof: if the roof held, the water streamed off, if it did not, then the firefighters were at serious risk from cascades of falling slates and molten lead. The requirements of HM Customs and the provisions of the Liverpool Building Acts of 1825–43 enforced standards of construction which at least inhibited the spread of fire, so that Liverpool never suffered a conflagration such as that which devastated a large area of Hamburg in 1842. Destructive fires on a less catastrophic scale remained fairly commonplace and ensured that fear of fire was kept very much alive.[58]

An even stronger disincentive was the politico-financial one. When Liverpool eventually achieved that long-sought status of a warehousing port, large amounts were invested by individuals and small companies in the provision of warehousing which met the fairly exacting security standards of the Crown. The building of warehouses on the quays by the Dock Committee would devalue those investments which were estimated in 1838 at nearly two million pounds. This was plainly a serious matter for the investors, who also argued with some justification that it was not necessarily in the interests of the town at large that such a devaluation should occur. Accusations flew around concerning violations of trust, the misfortune of widows and orphans whose sole source of income was investment in warehousing were agonized upon and it was pointed out that if warehouses were built within the dock walls it would be necessary to levy poor rates on the whole dock estate.[59] In the long term, warehouse building reverted to locations away from the docks, which rather justifies the arguments of their opponents to dockside warehouses.

The first stage in improving security on the quaysides was the building of perimeter walls pierced only by a small number of gateways which could be guarded by the dock police. One of the gestures made by the Dock Committee to help gain warehousing status was the agreement in 1805 – five years before any definite design had been produced – that Princes Dock would be built fully

A portion of the boundary wall at Princes, with a new (1873) police hut in the foreground
(Colin Pitcher)

enclosed by such a wall.[60] When the 1811 Dock Act was obtained, authorizing Rennie's design for Princes Dock, the power to build this wall was obtained, though only after overcoming quite strenuous opposition from the Leeds & Liverpool Canal Company who had extended their basins to a point just within the east side of the present-day King Edward Industrial Estate with a view to building a flight of locks down into Princes Dock. The same Act authorized the establishment of the dock police and of the division of fines imposed under the bye-laws between the informant and the Charitable Fund administered by the Dock Committee. Little evidence has survived of the day-to-day duties of those first Dock Constables, but on 25 July 1823, the Audit Commissioners were given some statistics of their activities which revealed that among other things, there had been 5,761 convictions for bye-law offences between October 1815 and October 1821 as against only 430 for misdemeanours. This was better news for the beneficiaries of the Charitable Fund than it was for HM Customs.

In 1836, Superintendent Dowling gave evidence on the workings of the dock police to a House of Commons Committee which made it clear that by then they were almost entirely concerned with bye-law offences. Very large numbers of charges were made – usually several dozen per week – relating to offences which varied from the trivial to the potentially disastrous. The 'pilfering and plunder' which the perimeter wall at Princes was meant to stop seems to have occupied relatively little of their time, and may support the view of the 1838 objectors to warehouse building that it was 'well known that petty thefts are as frequent within the walls of the docks as in the present warehouses'. It may be added in passing that Superintendent Dowling's evidence resulted in a prolonged 'carpeting' by the Dock Committee, who were far from pleased by the revelations he had made.[61]

When the wall at Princes was built, however, all this lay well in the future. Constant pressures had been exerted by the Crown to ensure that a wall would be built, and that it would be of substantial proportions.[62] In the event it was built about sixteen feet high (varying a little from place to place) of local brick in English Bond with substantial stone copings. In some places the upper part was four courses thick and the foundations six courses, the difference being accounted for by a two-course batter on the external side only while in others it was of four courses throughout. The finances of the construction of the dock had been an ongoing disaster, but the delay in completion of the wall was such that one suspects a certain lack of enthusiasm accompanied the overspending problem. Despite the suggestions that it was not very effective in preventing pilferage, it was to be the pattern for dock construction for the rest of the century, and to have a fundamental effect on the townscape of Liverpool. From now, Liverpudlians would be able to see their river and the ships which generated the wealth of the town from a dwindling number of vantage points, as the great walls, first of brick, later of

General view of a late (c. 1852) Hartley shed roof truss. Note the bridled purlins, a standard feature until the adoption of steel

(Colin Pitcher)

Jesse Hartley's cyclopean granite, spread north and south until they extended nearly five miles. They may have been partly responsible for a psychological division between the docks and the town in the latter part of last century which was almost as visible as the walls themselves.

Within the wall at Princes, there was little enthusiasm for the building of the warehouses for which the Crown kept pressing, indeed the building even of open transit sheds was delayed until 1824, when it was finally completed in response to a strongly-worded petition from local underwriters and merchants who were understandably annoyed

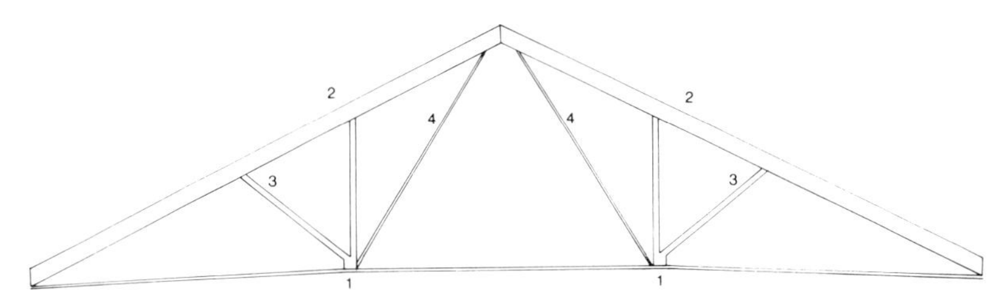

Fig. 3 *Composite roof truss,* c. *1870. The main intermediate design between the Hartley wooden truss and the turn-of-the-century all steel type. 1. Cast iron joint shoe 2. Timber principals 3. Timber compression members 4. Wrought iron tension members*

that Liverpool's largest, newest and most expensive dock should fail to offer even the most rudimentary protection against the elements for the cargoes on the quays.[63] The sheds were designed by Jesse Hartley shortly after his appointment on 24 March that year. It is not beyond the bounds of possibility that the reason for this delay was that materials, which had been ordered and paid for by John Foster, for the building of the sheds had been misappropriated for use by Foster's own joinery firm. Certainly some explanation is necessary for the fact that the work was ordered to be carried out on 25 January 1822 and a relatively simple construction remained unstarted twenty-six months later and the proven theft of timber may provide it. No drawings of these first open sheds have survived, but Nicholson's survey of 1827 reveals that there were three each side of the dock, two of them 515 ft long and the third 350 ft long, and that they were of the conventional kind already in use in the South Docks.

Whether this decision to build old-style open sheds was occasioned by the need for parsimony or to protect the warehousing *status quo*, they did nothing to ease either the need or the pressure for secure storage for bonded goods at or very close to the point of landing, and by the late 1830s serious controversy had broken out again, with demands for a range of warehouses on the west side of Princes. In the event, the issue would not be resolved at Princes, but at Albert, for in the 1841 Dock Act, powers were obtained to build a range of secure transit sheds on the west side of Princes Dock. These buildings were of four-course brick construction with timber-lined slate roofs, and represented a new 'half-way house' between the high security multi-storey warehouse and the no-security open shed. They were equipped

The heyday of the transit shed. This one at West Trafalgar actually dates from 1932, but it is the best surviving example of the landscape mentioned in the text
(Colin Pitcher)

with heavy wooden sliding doors twelve feet wide, of which the most significant feature was that, for the first time on sheds, they carried the double staple and hasp. One staple could be used for a Crown lock: they were approved for short-term storage of bonded goods.[64]

These new sheds started a fundamental change in the appearance of the port. Old-style open sheds continued in use, and a few new ones would yet be built, but the building of secure sheds gained momentum, and many of the older open sheds were enclosed to achieve similar results. The shed which stood at East Princes until 1929 was a good example of such a conversion, and the vestigial remains of a similar shed at East Canning still stand. The practice of shed-building evolved to what might be considered a classic form in the 1890s, and the surviving sheds of 1904–5 at the south end of West Princes are examples of the kind. The predominant landscape of the port became not a vision of lofty warehouses, but a succession of long avenues flanked by single-storey brick buildings, often several hundred yards long, the monotony of their appearance heightened by the grim colouring of soot-stained local brick, dark Welsh slate roofs and often dark-coloured Welsh paving setts as well. The introduction of the two-storey brick shed added a little variety in the South Docks from 1884, while the three-storey ferro-concrete shed, introduced at Sandon Dock in 1908 brought an element of ugliness which appears to have been axiomatic in the early days of the Hennebique system. These developments did not affect the Central Docks, whose appearance continued to be dominated over most of their area by the single-storey secure transit shed, overlooked only occasionally by nobler structures such as the Stanley Dock Warehouses or the Waterloo Corn Warehouses. Modernization programmes, of which that of 1904–5 was the most extensive, long continued only to reinforce the transit sheds' dominance by adding bigger, better and longer sheds, notably those at East Princes and West Trafalgar, each slightly over 500 yards long.

During the Second World War, some two linear miles of transit shed were destroyed, but because there was no inkling at the end of the war of the fundamental changes in the nature of goods handling and transit which would come about relatively soon, much of that capacity was reinstated, and the first really visible change was not heralded until the building of new passenger terminals at East and West Princes for the Dublin and Belfast ferries in 1953 and 1954 respectively. This slightly half-hearted updating, still based mostly on the use of the traditional transit sheds, gave way to the new coastal terminal based on the infilled Victoria Dock and the quayside of West Waterloo, which involved a major breach of the perimeter wall and a container-based open-air cargo-handling system. Opened in 1971, this development broke a pattern which had been established not by commercial or engineering desiderata but by crime in the 1820s and a compromise response to the problems it posed. It may come as no surprise that the last few yards of brickwork of the sheds which, completed in 1843, established such a durable pattern, still stand at the time of writing.

CHAPTER THREE

1848 – *ANNUS MIRABILIS*

The earliest Liverpool Docks tended to be fairly square in shape and each to have their own entrance to the river from a tidal outer basin. In the absence of an accumulated experience in dockbuilding, this was a logical way of tackling the problem of dock extension, particularly as it had the advantage of minimal disruption to traffic in the existing docks. It had serious disadvantages, though, and these were drawn to the attention of the Dock Committee by the report of William Jessop, made in 1800,[1] on the proposed new dock to the north of the Pier Head which would eventually be named Princes Dock. The purpose of a tidal basin was to allow a sailing vessel to approach at sufficiently high speed to retain steerage, and enter the basin via a wide passage. Once inside, the vessel was brought under control and warped into the relatively small entrance passage of the dock proper by the use of hand-operated capstans both on the vessel and on the quayside. Prior to the arrival of steam tugs, entering a lock direct from the river under sail would have been a pretty hair-raising experience if wind and tide did not permit coming alongside the Pier Head, as both the water and the air of the Mersey have a habit of moving rapidly, and more or less at right angles to the directions of the entrances. The tidal basin provided room to come to a halt in still water, and safe queuing and waiting moorings.

Against that had to be set the fact that a tidal basin was almost entirely useless for any other purpose except landing fish, and it represented a couple of acres of water enclosed from the river at an expense only slightly less than that of an equivalent area of wet dock. A more serious problem, and the one which Jessop regarded as crucial, was silt. Then as now, the Mersey carried a heavy burden of

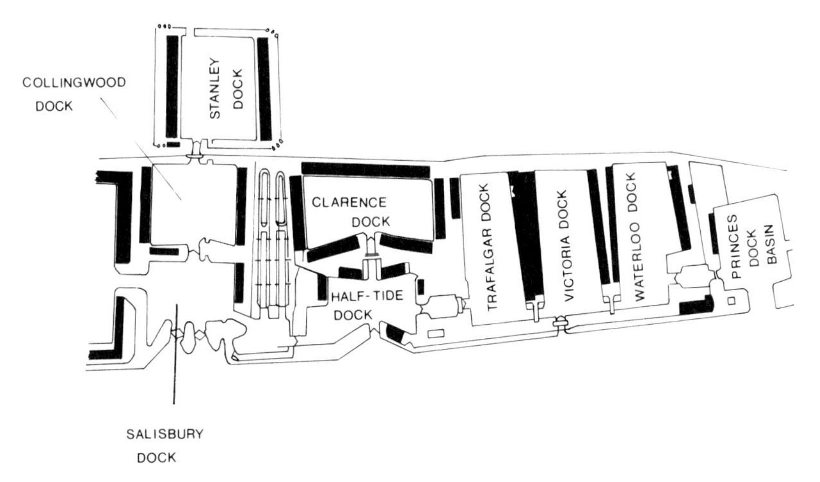

Fig. 4 Central Docks 1848. Note that Stanley Warehouses were only a proposal at this date. The small locks at Salisbury and Collingwood were originally covered as small 'tunnels'. Victoria entrance was closed and plugged by 1848, but not obliterated

fine silt. At water speeds above half a knot it remained in suspension, but a tidal basin was an ideal place for decelerating the water flow and thus causing it to be deposited. This had caused trouble and expense with the first dock, necessitating frequent 'cleansing' of the basin known as the Old Dock Gut, but could only get worse as vessels got larger and tidal basins as a result got deeper. Well before Princes Dock was built, it was clear that the Old Dock Sill was not deep enough for the largest vessels using the port, much less did it allow for any likely growth of ships in the future, so the decision was taken that the Princes Dock Sill should be six feet below Old Dock Sill.[2] This produced exactly the silting problems which Jessop had forecast, resulting in the need for expensive and less than entirely successful measures to keep the basins clear. Despite the employment of a steam dredger from the early date of 1823 and of the practice of letting impounded water from the dock at low water to sluice away the silt, it was none the less necessary to adopt the primitive and expensive expedient of having a gang of men ground a flat in the basin at a low water spring tide, jump out, and shovel silt into the flat until such time as either it was full or the returning tide compelled them to desist.[3]

As vessels grew larger, they also got less numerous in relation to the length of quay space available, because what governed the duration of their stay at the quayside (except when the weather intervened either by becalming them there or by being so rough as to make departure dangerous) was the rate at which goods could be discharged or loaded. This in turn depended on handling facilities and even more on the local transport infrastructure for getting goods to and from the quays. The larger the cross-section of the ship the slower the process and the more important the craneage. Other factors, such as delay in inspection by Customs of goods landed, could arise, but until the 1840s there was no significant rise in the rates at which goods were handled. The practical result was that fewer vessels needed to use any given entrance on any given tide, so that the 'queuing up' facility, which had been an important secondary advantage of the old tidal basin system, became relatively less important, while the ability to handle deeper vessels became more important.

In terms of the state of knowledge of dock building when the Act for the Princes Basin was obtained in 1811, it could be argued that the use of a tidal entrance was simply an adherence to an existing practice which had worked with tremendous commercial success at every entrance built in Liverpool up to that time. It is probably an unreasonable use of hindsight to suggest that the correctness of Jessop's view should have been obvious to people who were merely continuing to back a proven and highly profitable winner. Those entrances higher up the river which used entrance locks would be considered so small as not to constitute a relevant comparison.[4]

It appears at first sight that Jesse Hartley was quick to learn this lesson, for the next dock opened to the north, Clarence Dock, had a half-tide basin. A half-tide basin may be thought of as an oversized entrance lock: it is a dock with a single pair of gates which may be opened, as the name implies, at any time on the top half of the tide, and the levels left to follow the tide. Once the gate is shut again, the passage gates of the inner, fully impounded, docks may be opened to allow vessels to pass through. In practice it was obviously desirable to restrict the opening of the outer gates to times as close to high water as was feasible in order to minimize silt deposition and also variations in water level in the fully impounded docks, which had to provide the water to refill the half-tide basin to their level. The passage to the

Fig. 5 Jesse Hartley, Dock Surveyor 1824–60

inner dock has a single pair of gates facing inwards, which therefore acts as a giant non return valve: if the level in the half-tide exceeds that within, water will pass inwards, but if the level within exceeds that without, the gates will prevent loss of water. Many of the gates had back springs, to assist this one-way action.

The next new dock to be opened shows the learning of an even more important lesson, namely that it is better to minimize the number of entrances and maximize the size and quality of those considered essential. Waterloo, opened in 1834, did not have its own river entrance, but was reached by a lock and passage from Princes Basin. The lesson was a very simple one: entrances meant expense, both in construction and in manning and maintenance. Provided the docks did not become grossly overcrowded, it was clearly preferable for vessels to move around by warping within the system rather than by sailing in and out of a multiplicity of entrances. Clarence Dock had originally been built with the intention of achieving complete isolation of steam vessels,[5] which were seen as a serious fire hazard, from sailing vessels and from the small number of warehouses which were close enough to the quayside to be at risk from fire arising on board vessels, and thus it had to have its own distinct entrance. However, once pressure on space within the docks had translated itself into pressure on the foreshore and the decision had been taken to construct other docks adjacent to Clarence, there was no reason why these should not avail themselves of the Clarence half-tide entrance. A passage through to Trafalgar Dock was therefore provided, which made it possible, in theory at least, to work a vessel right through from Clarence, then the northern extremity, to Salthouse without the need to go out into the river and re-enter. In practice, of course, such a laborious 'voyage' should never have been necessary, but it illustrates the change which had occurred in the docks, which could by now reasonably be called a system rather than merely an accumulation of separate docks and basins. In 1846 this process was taken a stage further when it was decided that the entrance to Victoria Dock (1836) was superfluous, and it was therefore closed, access to Victoria now being either from Princes Basin via Waterloo Dock or from Clarence half-tide via Trafalgar.[6]

In a career such as Jesse Hartley's it is difficult to choose anything which might be considered to be his masterwork. One of the less spectacular claimants to the title is, at first sight, the completion of the complex of docks opened in 1848, namely Salisbury, Collingwood, Stanley, Nelson and Bramley-Moore. They were of

Salisbury entrance in 1980. The ground surface, which looks so smooth it might be of brick paviours, is in fact of precision-dressed granite: it is another of the 'certain places' (NMGM)

Date-stone at Salisbury entrance (NMGM)

modest size: Bramley-Moore was the largest with a water area under ten acres and there was no passage wider than 60 ft. In another sense, these docks represent the maturity of Hartley's vision of the dock estate. Designed and built as a group, they contain samples of practically every one of Hartley's dock building skills from the typically massive granite gravity basin walls, and an equally massive granite boundary wall, through severely practical minor buildings such as the gateman's house and the well-proven double-leaf iron swing bridges which he used almost everywhere, to the novel yet highly functional six-faced clock tower at Salisbury entrance[7] and a touch of medievalist fantasy in the Stanley Hydraulic Pumping Station. Stanley was also equipped with two stacks of warehouses very similar to those at Albert, which had the same quality of achieving aesthetic merit almost by accident while in pursuit of a purely functional objective. Everything which Hartley had learned, whether from others or from the evolution of his own outstanding talents, was incorporated in this coherent programme. Although the individual docks were relatively small, taken together they represent the largest extension made up to that time, and the formidable problems of design and management they posed were overcome in a way in which Foster before him and Lyster after proved incapable.

The beautifully constructed entrance at Salisbury was not only a double half-tide entrance like the one Hartley had completed in his remodelling of the Old Dock Gut to form Canning Half-Tide Dock, it also had a small lock capable of admitting flats and other small vessels at almost any state of the tide with only minimal effect on the

View across the flat lock and Salisbury to Collingwood and Stanley beyond. The lock really is of red sandstone (partly). Note the small lock to Collingwood (referred to in the text) in the middle ground

(Colin Pitcher)

The clock tower at Salisbury entrance, with residences beyond
(NMGM)

water-level in the half-tide basin. There were similar small locks through from the half-tide to Collingwood and from Collingwood to Stanley, to prevent delays to small craft occurring as a result of variations in levels between the different fully impounded docks.

By this time, the idea was thoroughly accepted that docks might, and in many cases should, specialize in a particular traffic. Much was made, in the evidence for obtaining the Act for this programme, of the need to free Brunswick Dock of traffics other than timber, in order that it might specialize in what it was best for, and conversely that the system should ensure that all timber went to Brunswick. In this particular case the reason was obvious, for timber was discharged by dropping it overside into the dock, and later hauling it out onto the side: Brunswick Dock at this period, therefore, resembled a rectangular slipway rather than a dock in the normal sense of the term, and was notably unsuitable for the discharge of, for example, cotton. This was also a time when the importing of Canadian timber was growing rapidly. John Easton, the dockmaster at Brunswick, gave evidence that the flag had been hoisted (indicating that the dock was full) on 251 days of the previous year.

Steamers were by now finding the Clarence Dock far too small: its 50 ft entrance had been left behind by the rapid growth of vessels, and the general opinion was that for transatlantic steamers 70 ft was now needed. More important, perhaps, was the fact that increased experience in the berthing and discharge of steamers revealed that Clarence was really the wrong shape. Sailing vessels could, and often did, discharge three abreast at the quay and could also be berthed diagonally or even end-on to the quay with only some inconvenience in discharging. Steamers, because of the width of their paddle boxes, could not. The reason that owners were prepared to pay the much higher capital costs of steamers was their higher availability (i.e. more voyages per year) and the premium which was placed on a faster turn-round in port meant that owners argued strongly for provision of docks which would allow every steamer a full-length side-on berth promptly on its arrival. That, in turn, meant that docks needed proportionally more quay space to water space than in relatively square docks like Clarence.[8]

Bramley-Moore was intended to take the largest of these craft, with Nelson capable of taking equally large vessels, but normally taking those a little smaller. Each of these docks was more than twice as long as it was wide, but neither in the event had access for vessels over 60 ft wide, which meant that their 'flagship' role was purely temporary, to last only until the completion of Sandon and Wellington Docks, with their 70 ft entrance and passages, three years later and the even larger Huskisson Dock in 1852. Inland of the half-tide Salisbury Dock was the fairly square Collingwood Dock, intended for smaller vessels, and beyond that Stanley, intended mainly for the coasting trade and for traffic interchange via the Leeds and Liverpool Canal.

One of the main constraints on the speed of discharge of vessels had always been the availability of carts to remove goods from open quays or transit sheds, and the growing pressure for faster turn-round of steamships made this problem more prominent. The relatively small carts used to remove goods to consignees' premises or to public warehouses simply could not handle goods at anything like the speed they could be discharged from a vessel, neither could they deliver them fast enough for loading. The connection to the Leeds and

Liverpool Canal was not just a matter of saving the shilling per ton which cartage cost (and on an estimated 150,000 tons of Wigan coal brought down the canal for export in 1842 that was a substantial saving), it was also a matter of allowing ships to load or discharge overside to or from a canal boat, thus easing the pressure on the quayside. This reflects the understanding by the Dock Committee and by Hartley of the simple fact that a port is first and foremost about handling goods: of course the handling of ships is important, but it is the goods they carry which are the *raison d'etre* of the port and to concentrate on ship-handling at the expense of goods handling is to put the cart before the horse.[9]

The accusation is often levelled at the Port of Liverpool that it embraced full cooperation with the railways far too late and with little ardour, and there is sufficient evidence in the latter part of the century to justify this. It is not, however, justified in the days of Jesse Hartley. Stanley Dock having proved the worth of the connection with the canal, would also be connected both with the Lancashire and Yorkshire Railway, and with the dock railway, work on which began in 1850.[10]

Behind the extension programme of the 1844 Act, which included, it should be remembered, Wellington and Sandon Docks as well as the five opened in 1848 lay the ongoing works of construction of Albert Dock and the remodelling which resulted in Canning half-tide achieving its present form. This laid the Dock Committee open to accusations of building far in advance of proven demand, taking unacceptable risks with very large sums of money which were mostly raised by bond debt – in effect by mortgaging future revenues. Such accusations may have had some justification in the minds of the more cautious, but the figures for tonnage using the port gave little support for such a view. A tabulation produced in 1841 reveals that since the last extension to the system was completed in 1836, tonnage had increased by nearly a third. Looking further back, it had doubled in the fifteen years since work had begun on Canning Dock and more than trebled since the completion of Princes Dock in 1821. Over the same twenty years, the average tonnage of vessels using the port had risen from 107.5 tons to 150.5.[11] If these increases were indeed just a run of luck, it was a run such as most gamblers would continue to back, and one is tempted to suspect other motives than mere caution in the minds of the objectors to the scheme. The prolonged and bitter wrangling which had continued since the 1820s over the proposed building of docks on Wallasey Pool, across the river, had eventually been resolved, after a fashion, by the sale of land which the Liverpool Dock Committee owned there. It had always been clear that the purpose of Liverpool's ownership of that land was the prevention of unwanted competition, with the result that the protagonists of docks on the Wirral side were becoming fairly bitter and suspicious people. To them, it seemed quite clear that Liverpool, having at last released the land needed for the Wirral Docks, was now seeking to bankrupt them by an expansion programme so massive as to leave no foreseeable traffic available for the infant competitor. The result was some very strident opposition, and probably a hidden motivation for other objections of a less open nature.

The allegation that Liverpool deliberately built these docks to forestall developments on the other side assumes that the Dock Committee was seriously worried by the schemes. This may be correct, though one cannot but suspect that Jesse and John Hartley knew their trade well enough to tell from the proposals for Birkenhead that there was not a great deal to fear, at least in the short term. Whether or not they did, events were to prove that such was the case. The Birkenhead Dock Commissioners' ability for shooting themselves in the foot was sufficient to suggest that they might have anticipated the invention of the machine gun. When their works began in 1844, they formed an object lesson in financial mismanagement, intrigue and engineering failure such as is only rarely encountered in the history of any port. They blundered through crisis to disaster to catastrophe until 1855, when their works had to be taken over by Liverpool for the superior talents of J.B. Hartley, backed by superior financing and management, to sort out the mess which had resulted.[12] The Liverpool Dock Committee knew how to build and operate docks: their would-be competitors did not, and spending money on a 'big name' engineer could not make good that deficiency.

The works on the Liverpool side, by contrast, proceeded with speed and efficiency. The new group of docks involved more excavation than in most previous projects, and Stanley Dock is unique in the Liverpool system in being entirely excavated from dry land. Much of the spoil would in fact be usable red sandstone, with the result that Hartley's natural parsimony, perhaps spurred on by occasional accusations of building *folies de grandeur*, came into conflict with his love for the use of Kirkmabreck granite. In his evidence before the Parliamentary Committee, he had stated that 'no granite is to be used except in certain places'. The certain places in which it was used turned out to be all four walls of all five docks together with most of the masonry of the entrance and passages, copings, nosings, the paving of the entrance islands and the steps provided for boatmen. Red sandstone was used for the gate housings and for the walls of the boatlock between Salisbury and Collingwood, though not for the boat 'tunnel' under the east quay of Collingwood and the Dock Road. Work began in August 1844, and spoil was removed at a considerable rate – 655,000 cubic yards in the first year, or over 1,000 tons per working day – which rather suggests that it was not being carefully removed for recovery of useful building stone. In that same year the foundations of 700 yards of river wall and 1,000 yards of dock wall were laid. By summer 1847, the volume excavated had topped 3,000,000 cubic yards and all but 1,599 yards of the walls were complete. The dock walls were 33 feet high and the river wall 37½ feet high, and the gates and passages were described as being well advanced. So too, however, was the expenditure, which already exceeded by some £12,000 the estimate of £507,465 which Hartley had given in 1844.[13]

The construction of this group of docks is marked by another of the 'windows' of information which occasionally illuminate our view of the way that civil engineering works actually proceeded on the ground. The work coincided with the latter stages of the boring of the notorious Woodhead Tunnel on the Sheffield, Ashton under Lyne and Manchester Railway, which employed up to 1,500 navvies at a time. Edwin Chadwick pointed out that the rate of fatal accidents on the project was 3 per cent, whereas the average for deaths of private soldiers over the battles of Talavera, Salamanca, Vittoria and Waterloo was 2.11 per cent, and that a further 14 per cent of the navvies were 'wounded'. In addition to this, they were shamelessly exploited by the tommy shops run by the contractors, and the logistics of supplying them with the necessities of life in the remote Pennine districts in which they were working would have been considered inadequate by Lord Raglan.[14] Even in an age which placed a much lower value on human life, and a higher value on landed property, than we do today, such facts were profoundly shocking to HM Government. Woodhead, like many other projects, totally brutalized the men working on it, and liberal members of the Government were inclined to think that the frequent orgies of robbery, violence, drunkenness, gluttony and plain old-fashioned carnal lust which so scandalized all who heard of them could possibly be the product of the circumstances in which the men worked. The result was the appointment of a Select Committee on Railway Labourers, and the last witness to give evidence was our outspoken friend of a former chapter, Superintendent Dowling, by now Commissioner of Police for Liverpool.[15]

His evidence has little to do with railway construction, although there is some mention of construction of the Liverpool & Bury Railway – the line out of Exchange Station which is always associated with the name of the Lancashire and Yorkshire Railway. Most of his evidence is concerned with the construction of the new docks at the north end of the estate, and perhaps the clearest message we receive from it is that remarked upon in the context of the construction of Princes Dock, namely that the men employed by the Dock Committee enjoyed vastly better conditions than those endured by the men working for contractors. There were about 4,000 men working on the scheme between August 1844 and June 1846, of whom about 2,800 were contractors' men and 1,800 were directly employed by Hartley. Dowling does not explain the arithmetical discrepancy, but it is probably safe to assume that the extra 600 men were replacements for the dead, the injured and the 'slopers' (those who disappeared because their drinking or gambling debts made them incapable of paying the rent on their accommodation).

The accident rate to the contractors' men was, on a project inherently safe compared with tunnelling, quite appalling. In the space of twenty-two months, 118 out of 2,800 had been seriously injured and 11 killed 'on the spot'. Of the 118, 18 had died almost immediately in the hospital, and Commissioner Dowling was unable to say how many more had died after being taken home. No attempt was made to record minor injuries, which raises the question of what constituted a serious injury. From hospital returns produced by other witnesses, a serious injury appears to have been one which involved the breakage of any bone larger than finger-bones and superficial wounds involving serious loss of blood.

The fact which caused serious eyebrow-raising on the committee, however, was not the level of casualties among the contractors' men: the evidence of previous days had probably rendered them immune to any sentiments of surprise or outrage. What did surprise them was that during the same twenty-two months, of Jesse Hartley's 1,800 men none had been killed and just two seriously injured. Clearly if that discrepancy could be explained, then application of the secrets of Hartley's success in not killing his men might result in dramatic improvements in the safety record of railway companies. It is curious that they did not coax Jesse himself out through his granite portals in Liverpool to give evidence, but in his absence Dowling gave a very cogent and surprisingly simple explanation.

In the main, contractors' men were doing the cutting and excavation, and Hartley's men were doing the masonry work. While the masonry work could possibly be portrayed as inherently safer, it involved the handling of thousands of extremely heavy pieces of irregular shaped stone with rather rudimentary equipment, and provided plenty of scope for dropping the said heavy pieces of stone onto people from heights of thirty feet or more. In short it was necessary to look somewhere other than the inherent danger of the work. The contractors' men were working in the manner which had become customary in the excavation of canals and railways, namely that the principal contractor in effect, though not in law, subcontracted the removal of 'muck' (as navvies termed any material whatever that needed to be removed) to gangers at an agreed rate per cubic yard. In the case of linear works like railways a further intermediary, the 'hagman', might be involved, but this did not happen in Liverpool Docks because communication was inherently easier. The principal technical and managerial skills possessed by a typical ganger were two in number: his left fist and his right. His interest was in output; safety came somewhere well below Z in his alphabet.[16]

The usual method of working when digging a cutting or a deep hole such as a dock was to start a working face and then proceed from that by undercutting, so as to cause the muck to collapse, rendering itself easy to shovel. There was nothing dangerous in such a procedure, provided that the working face was not so high, or the undercuts so deep, that when it fell it crushed or buried the men below. Imminent collapse could almost invariably be anticipated – and warning given to those below – by an experienced man watching from above, a duty eminently suitable for older navvies or those disabled in previous accidents. The financial imperatives of the job ensured that all of these conditions for safe working were ignored, with the result that collapses of undercut faces were the main cause of accident. Similarly, the barrow run on which a horse drew a barrow full of muck, steered by a navvy, up a narrow timber ramp out of the hole, was open to some possibility of safe operation. Used by men in a hurry who were often half drunk (or more) it rated second to collapses as a cause of death and injury.

Where, as at Stanley Dock, rock was encountered, blasting also took its toll. The method was to bore a hole in the rock with a jumper drill and hammer, as used in the quarry trades until quite recently, insert a charge of black powder, compress it in the hole with a rammer, apply a fuse, plug the mouth of the hole, and ignite the powder. There were simple and well-known means of avoiding the obvious potential for accident, in particular the use of a copper rammer (which could not strike a spark from the rock) and of either a patent fuse or 'the galvanic wire'. These all cost money, with the result that men continued to be killed and maimed by ramming charges with iron rammers and firing them with straws filled with black powder.

There were those, of course, who would attribute this state of affairs to the large number of Irish navvies, driven straight off the land by poverty of the grossest kind, who came to work at the docks and obtained their jobs by lying about their previous experience or absence of it. To these, the ignorant, must be added a large number of the better-informed who were none the less utterly stupid and reckless. It must be conceded that it is only quite recently that some sections of industrial workers have ceased to regard anyone who took sensible precautions such as wearing ear-defenders or protective headgear as a nancy-boy and there can be little doubt that such peer group pressures to live dangerously were a contributory cause of the navvy's poor life expectancy. The fact of the matter was that 'a good portion of them were Irish, but there are others who are Lancashire men . . . (the Irish) . . . are the most reckless violent sort of people that can be imagined'. No figures are given, but the implication is that the Irish were only a substantial minority who drew attention to themselves by their behaviour off the site.[17]

The life of a navvy was undoubtedly nasty, brutish and short, and his miseries were often compounded by the fact that, not being technically employed by the contractor, he was denied the protection of the Truck Act, and was therefore liable to be exploited through the tommy shop. The principal consolation in the face of these and other miseries was alcohol, often in huge amounts, and even this pleasure was subject to depredations in the beer shop run by a ganger or by the travelling whisky seller (a sort of two-legged St Bernard, with a small cask hung round his neck) who paid his percentage for access to the site and charged inflated prices to cover this outgoing. When pay-day came around the inevitable consequence was a 'randy', featuring all manner of mayhem and drunkenness: 'They keep the neighbourhood where they reside, which is in the north part of the town of Liverpool, in a constant state of uproar and confusion on Saturday nights, Sundays and Mondays and generally a portion of Tuesday.' Faced with the police, they would defend each other to desperate lengths, not hesitating to use their pointed cutting spades as weapons, and Dowling knew better than to allow his men to get involved in such dangerous situations unless they could be there in 'overwhelming force', indeed he admitted that in some circumstances the presence of the police could itself be the main cause of the disorder. Asked if he had tried to plant undercover men among the navvies, he stated that he had not because it was too dangerous. The committee had heard enough from previous witnesses to realize that dismissal was probably a more effective deterrent than prison, but when asked, Dowling responded that his attempts to make the contractors take an interest in the mayhem their men caused had invariably met with denials that the particular man in question worked for the contractor approached.

By contrast, Hartley's men verged on the angelic. The reasons which were adduced for this mainly related to the fact that they were better managed and better treated. The key to the lower accident rate was that at all times their working sites were under the supervision of an engineer from the dockyard who provided guidance and, if necessary, instruction on correct and therefore safe working practices, and expected them to be employed. A secondary factor was that most of the unskilled or semi-skilled men were working as labourers assisting Hartley's team of highly skilled masons, who undoubtedly had different working values from those of gangers whose sole objective was to shift as much muck as quickly and as cheaply as possible. The men paid 2d per week into a fund for

sickness or injury pay and this money, together with any entitlement to help from the Charitable Fund, was forfeit if they were dismissed for serious misconduct. Dowling denied that Hartley's men were 'of a different class' from those employed by the contractors, but his description of the consequences of their better management and treatment makes it clear that they were of a different calibre.

There were, of course, consequences for the town other than the disorder of the 'randies'. A disabled navvy would almost certainly end up on parish relief, but before he got to that stage he had already cost the parish overseers money in the hospital which had just been built on Great Howard Street specifically to 'receive patients from the numerous accidents constantly occurring to persons employed about the docks.'[18] Unfortunately, the parish overseers did not keep records in a form which allowed the separation of any figures relating to navvies, but figures presented to the Select Committee relating to railway works in other areas make it clear that the average navvy patient cost between £2 and £3 to treat. The vast majority of injuries were fractures of bones in the feet and legs, with broken arms and ribs next in frequency. A compound fracture of the leg could hospitalize a man for six months. Railway companies and their contractors made derisory donations to local hospitals – the South Western Railway Company, for example, donated £5 to Salisbury Hospital where an estimated £177 had been expended on treatment for injured navvies from their sites, and their principal contractor gave the less than princely sum of six guineas (£6.30).[19] Such figures are not available for Liverpool, but from Dowling's evidence there is no reason to suppose that they would not be roughly comparable.

It could be thought that evidence given to such a Select Committee would be of doubtful historical value on the grounds that the function of the committee was really to sit there and be shocked by the appalling behaviour of the lower orders and to produce a report filled with elegantly worded strictures thereon, perhaps enhanced with some constructive suggestions for hanging, transporting, or flogging rather more navvies. Such a view is not merely unsupported, but almost the exact opposite of the truth. The committee was sympathetic to the plight of the navvies, and called several as witnesses. It even raised the question of whether contractors ought not to be liable in civil law (as they were in France) for death or disablement of their workers if negligence could be proved. The idea was clearly accepted that the public benefits which accrued from canal, railway and port improvements were partly paid for in the human suffering of the navvies. Dowling, although at one stage recounting an attack of utmost brutality on one of his men, was able to consider the issue dispassionately and offer some constructive clues towards the causes and cures. The overwhelming conclusion is that navvies behaved bestially because they were bestially treated, and that where they were properly managed, as they were by Jesse Hartley, the problems were very greatly diminished. It is a matter for regret that his 'secret' was largely ignored by other engineers to such a degree that it was not until the mechanized carnage of the Great War that it became statistically safer to be a navvy than a soldier.

This account of the building of a group of docks has concentrated on practical matters at the expense of any consideration of the design process, and in particular of the scientific or theoretical basis of the most vital part of the work, the construction of the walls. In the process, that oldest of chestnuts in the history of the history of technology, the relationship between theory and practice, has also been avoided.

By the time construction started in 1844, the theory of retaining walls was well established. The first major contribution to the subject had been published as early as 1729 by Belidor, the famous French polymath.[20] He stated that the overturning forces on a wall could be calculated given the angle of repose of the earth in which it stood by imagining the triangular section of earth between the line represented by that angle and the inside face of the wall trying to slide downwards. His formula for the overturning moment with a 45° angle of repose was $wh^3/12$ where w is the weight per unit volume of the earth or fill behind the wall and h is the height of the wall. According to Timoshenko 'using the value of moment in calculating the thickness', Belidor arrives at proportions which are in agreement with the then established practice'. In 1773, Coulomb presented a much more sophisticated theory[21] which took account of cohesive forces along the predicted slip line and also any superimposed loads – such as goods on the quaysides. This work reputedly stood the test of time, for Timoshenko, in a section headed 'Theory of Retaining Walls and Arches between 1833 and 1867', tells us that 'During this period, engineers continued to use Coulomb's theory'.[22]

It is quite possible that French engineers, who were products of a highly organized professional training system quite unlike anything in England, did use Coulomb's theory, but there are no indications that Jesse Hartley did. His drawings of sections of walls do not have a slip line marked on them, nor any marking of the 1/3 point at which the overturning force acted, and no other signs of calculations have been discovered. Perhaps equally telling is the fact that many later copies of his drawings of wall sections exist, which were made when works of his were being modernized, and even to these, no indications of the application of Coulomb's theory have been added. Hartley may well have been aware of the theory, for his excavations were taken back to a slip line of 45°, but equally this may have been a simple matter of protecting his masons from the risk of slips while they were at work on the lower parts of the wall, and as we have seen, his outstanding safety record suggests that nothing of the kind was neglected.

Another place we might find some indications of application of Coulomb's theory was in the reconstruction of large amounts of the walling of Birkenhead Docks. The work at Birkenhead was a disaster in almost every possible way, including the employment of two different engineers, Abernethy and Rendel, who did not agree on very much, and the repeated withdrawal of contractors. One manifestation of these difficulties was the instability of much of the walling, and when J.B. Hartley went to sort it out, he undertook a considerable amount of demolition.[23] If there was a sound theory which was in normal current use, is it likely that he would have failed to invoke it in showing the need for such a drastic course of action as to demolish the work of an eminent man like Rendel and start again? In 1869, John Ellacot read a *Description of the Low Water Basin at Birkenhead* to the Institute of Civil Engineers[24] which refers to many of the problems of Birkenhead Docks but nowhere does he suggest that the walls were wrongly calculated. One is forced to the conclusion that the matter was simpler than that. Some of the walls at Birkenhead fell and others which had been built the same way became unstable: the Hartleys knew how to build walls which never fell and only very rarely became unstable.

This question of walls falling was not so unusual as we might imagine, and in a paper presented to 'The Civils' in 1858 [25] we find a clear explanation of some of the problems of wall-building and of systematic investigation and recording of failures. Robert Rawlinson made a contribution to the discussion on the paper which is notable for containing the only authoritative statement about the methods of Jesse Hartley, and neither there, nor in the paper itself, is there any mention of Coulomb or his theory. Since Rawlinson was explaining why Hartley's walls did not fall like some mentioned in the paper it seems inconceivable that he should fail to mention either that Hartley successfully applied Coulomb's theory, or that he thought it unreliable and dangerous and chose to ignore it. The only circumstances which would explain such an omission is that it was well understood that such walls were built on the basis of experience and judgement, not of calculation.

All this evidence is negative, and the sceptical reader might by now be wondering how one can be sure that the two Hartleys did not have little pocket books in which they did all their calculations, and which have not survived. It is true that such a possibility cannot be entirely ruled out, but we may turn to the evidence of one of the nineteenth century's most distinguished engineers to reinforce the arguments above. Benjamin Baker is best known for his work on the Forth Railway Bridge, but long before then he had been diligent in his attempts to marry theory and practice, originally in the structural aspects of bridge-building, but later in allied fields as well.

Timoshenko identified two main landmarks in the process of the adoption and improvement of theory in civil engineering in England. They were Barlow's *Treatise on the Strength of Materials* and Rankine's *Manual of Civil Engineering*.[26] The two writers were men who commanded great respect, and Rankine's work, both as a teacher of engineering at Glasgow and as the author of several very notable textbooks, gives him a good claim to be regarded as the leading figure in nineteenth-century university engineering.

Baker obviously regarded these works as very important as well, for in his paper to 'The Civils' *On the Actual Lateral Pressure of Earthworks*[27] he lays aside his rapier, picks up his bludgeon and wields it to good effect on Barlow and Rankine. The burden of the paper is that in the subject of retaining walls and of earthworks more generally, the theorists have been of virtually no service to the actual building of things because they failed to gather and use practical data from real structures. Of course he also criticizes, though more mildly, practical engineers like the Hartleys for not availing themselves of theoretical work. His claim is that his paper is the first to bring together theory and practice in this particular and intimate way.

Stanley passage, showing the neo-medieval Hydraulic Pumping Station (right) and the Boat 'Tunnel' (left). The double-deck swing bridge carried the Overhead Railway with the dock railway below, while the swing bridge in the foreground carried the Dock Road

(Liverpool City Engineer's Department)

Of course papers were usually claimed to be original, not always correctly, but in this case we may probably take Baker at his word. The paper is one of the longest published by 'The Civils', amounting, with its discussion and correspondence, to 101 pages, and it must be significant that neither in the discussion nor the correspondence is there any suggestion that what Baker said was not original, nor is he at any point taken to task for his attacks on the theorists. The picture which emerges is of theorists and practical engineers walking the same route in parallel, with little or no effective interchange of ideas or information. It is a picture presented by a man who was most certainly in a position to know the truth of the matter.

If the foregoing is true, then it would be reasonable to claim that Hartley built his walls on a basis of empirical craft experience and knowledge, backed up by very fine craftmanship. Such a statement is also true of the builders of Gothic cathedrals, and there really was no reason why Hartley should not have thought of himself as being in that tradition rather than the practitioner of a new and scientific form of engineering. The 1840s were a good time for neo-medievalism which had by then acquired an established literature, school of painting and sculpture, and architecture. In the few places where Jesse Hartley was allowed a touch of architectural whimsy, the rather classical lines of his utilitarian style disappear and we have police huts with arrow-slits and accumulator towers with castellations. His pumping station at Canada entrance was probably the most eccentric neo-medieval building in Liverpool.[28]

J.B. Hartley was responsible for the design (though not the construction) of the Hydraulic Tower at Birkenhead, which was a splendid piece in Italian Renaissance style until damaged in the Second World War. Just as J.B. Hartley had improved on oligarch palace design by having a standard gauge railway run in through the front door (for delivering coal to the boilerhouse) so his father had improved on medieval wall-building by the use of excellent hydraulic mortars and granite. That did not mean that he was outside the age-old traditions of masonry work.

It has been an enduring tradition of biographies of British engineers that they portray intuitive geniuses with little or no grounding in theory. Samuel Smiles did not actually invent this tradition, but he enlarged upon it with such success[29] that the effects of his writings are clearly visible to this day. As Buchanan has remarked, there is a huge preponderance of biographies of engineers who were dead by 1860[30] – an age when theory played a comparatively small part in engineering. Even in cases where a significant element of science or mathematics was involved, it has tended to be played down. We still speak of Robert Stephenson's tubular bridges, despite the fact that he could not have built them without the experiments and calculations carried out by Fairbairn and Hodgkinson. It is the genius of the conception, not the tedious scribbling and doing of the sums, which catches the imagination. The danger is that we might see Hartley as another larger-than-life romantic hero from the Smilesian mould of Brindley or George Stephenson.

On such evidence as has been found, it appears that such misgivings are unjustified. Hartley was a member of 'The Civils' for thirty-five years, and during that time he never presented a paper, nor even a contribution to a discussion, on the subject of his wall-building method. Despite his known dislike for going to London, this would be a little odd were we not able to assume that he probably saw nothing particularly worthy of note about his methods of building walls. They stood up better than anybody else's walls did, but that was through a thorough understanding of the 'proper way', detail improvements in materials, craft skills of the highest order and careful management and supervision. He was not practising any technique with which anyone was unfamiliar, he was just doing it better.

CHAPTER FOUR

OBSOLESCENCE, RAILWAYS AND COAL

The new group of docks was opened with due solemnities on 4 August 1848, but as was so often the case all that was really opened was five big holes in the ground filled with water. Work continued in snatches for another three years on items which were really quite essential for the efficient use of the docks. During the year following the opening, open sheds were built on the north and south sides of Collingwood and on the south side of Salisbury. By mid-1850 there were similar sheds on all four sides of Nelson and also a close (i.e. secure) brick shed on the west quay. Much of the open quay space had been paved by now, but paving of some areas at both Collingwood and Nelson had to wait another year, as did the provision of sheds at Bramley-Moore. A total of over £30,000 was spent on sheds alone in the first three years of operation.[1] Success was immediate, but proved short-lived, for the same changes and pressures which had justified the construction of this group of docks soon caused their downgrading from the prestige traffics in the largest vessels as Hartley's larger docks were completed to the north. As early as 1850 Hartley was required to report to the Dock Committee on the facilities for the shipping of coal in Liverpool Docks, a requirement which might not be unconnected with the impending presence of the Great Western Railway, with its access to the coalfields of the Wrexham area and of South Wales, on the Birkenhead Docks. That report identified the possibility of a specialized facility at Bramley-Moore Dock, and by 1855 the construction was 'in a forward state'.[2]

Even before that construction had started, Nelson Dock had become a victim of its own success, for by 1853 the Dock Committee

No photographs of the original open sheds of the 1848 docks have been located, but this shed at East Canning illustrates the design

(NMGM)

was receiving repeated complaints from a number of shipowners. The problem was the rapid adoption of screw steamers too large for the older docks in trades to and from mainland Europe. These vessels were used, and had to be used, intensively, many making more than one voyage a month. Wilson and Son complained repeatedly at their vessels being delayed for days at a time by the lack of suitable berths and/or shed space at Nelson Dock, including, for example, SS *Blarney*, delayed three days with a cargo of bonded goods in June 1854. John Bibby was another complainer: in December 1853 he had four ships waiting in Nelson 'to our very serious inconvenience and loss.' The smallest of these, *Arno*, was 190 ft long and *Calpe*, the

The same sheds at East Canning Dock viewed from the waterside
(NMGM)

largest, was 231 ft long. Between 1852–5, Bibby's added ten substantial screw steamers to their fleet, every one of them the size of a crack Atlantic liner of only ten years previous.[3] Nelson had, therefore, to slide further down the trading scale within just a few years of construction and the indignity to befall it was presaged in the Engineer's Report for 1852, where it is recounted ungrammatically that 'Three additional Watering-places for Horses and Cattle have been provided and in use'.

Prior to the passing of the Contagious Diseases (Animals) Act of

1878, it had been the normal practice to land livestock wherever a convenient berth was available, and in the evidence for the 1844 Bill the dockmaster of Clarence and Trafalgar Docks had testified to the suitability of the location of the new docks proposed: 'Cattle, Sheep, pigs etc. are driven away without inconvenience . . . Passengers are in a convenient part of the town.' The time would not be long in coming when cabin passengers arriving from America would not regard a berth next to a vessel discharging injured and seasick cattle as 'convenient', and as the larger vessels moved north, Nelson became the normal dock for discharge of livestock. An outbreak of cattle plague in Ireland in 1866 led to a decision that all Irish cattle, and only Irish cattle, should be discharged at Clarence and Collingwood Docks,[4] but repeated complaints followed that this instruction was not being observed, and by February 1867 Nelson was also receiving both Irish and Scottish cattle in quantities. On landing, the animals were examined and if found to be diseased were immediately dispatched in one of four temporary slaughterhouses erected at Collingwood, Clarence and Nelson Docks. In 1875, an assistant transit shed-keeper was 'carpeted' for putting sheep in No. 6 transit shed and in April the same year a Government Inspector ordered immediate slaughter of 478 sheep just landed there. After 1878, when most livestock had to be landed at specific dedicated berths known as Foreign Animals Wharves, the situation changed radically; but in 1876, 7,788 cattle and 14,452 pigs were landed in Liverpool by foreign trade alone, all at general purpose berths, and all in a fairly lackadaisical manner.[5]

What this substantial traffic concealed was the fact that Nelson and Collingwood Docks were already in need of modernization. It is understandable that the Dock Board should not have searched too diligently for evidence that such was the case, for they had enormous liabilities elsewhere. On the Wirral side, they had only just completed a large programme to deal with the last and greatest of the engineering disasters over there, the Great Low Water Basin, which had not only involved the remodelling of the basin into the present form of Wallasey Dock, but also the construction of a large river entrance which worked to replace the abandoned one which did not. Work, and massive expenditure, had already begun on the programme of works authorized by the Act of 1873 to improve and extend the Liverpool system at both the northern and southern

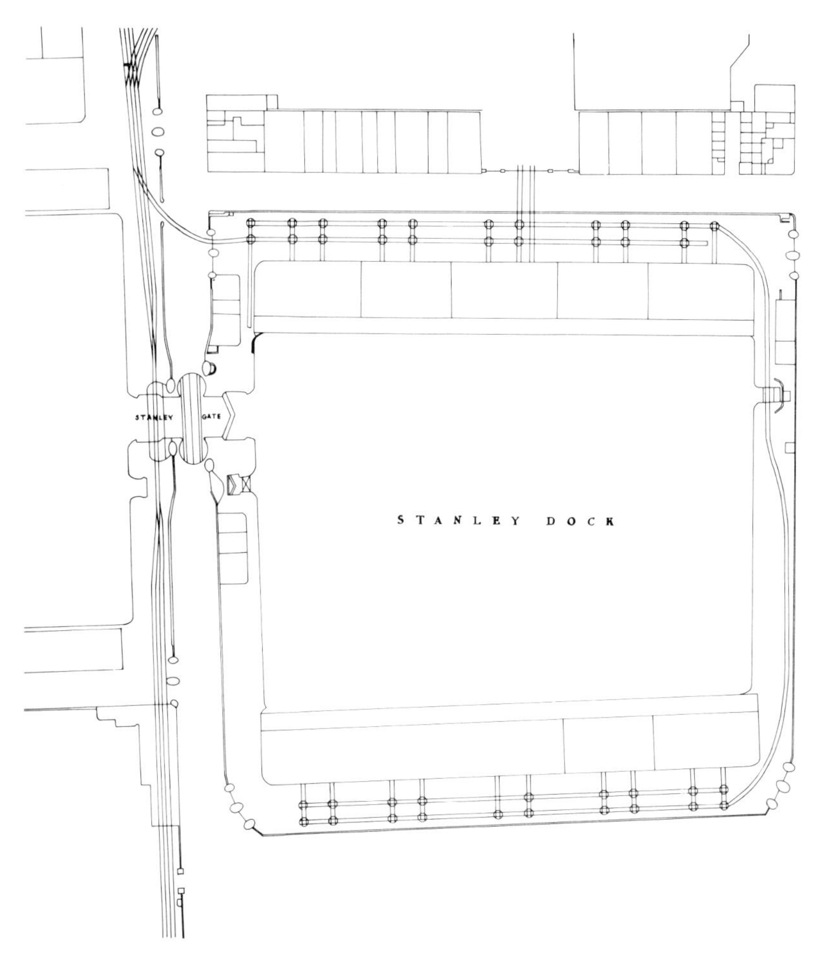

Fig. 6 *Stanley Dock* c. *1860, showing original arrangement of railway access to warehouses, using turntables*

extremities. The programme was of unprecedented extent, and its already huge cost in money and in staff time was noticeably increased by the indecision and errors remarked upon in Chapter Two. There really was no reason for the Board to consider spending scarce resources on a dock which appeared to be working quite successfully and handling plenty of traffic. No reason, that is, unless they had wished to follow the example of their predecessor body by attempting to stay ahead of demand and thus of the competition of other ports.

Stanley Dock had been envisaged from the outset as another fully enclosed dock like Albert, with warehouses within a boundary wall, to provide secure storage for high value, or more particularly for bonded, goods. Hartley's men began the excavation for the foundations of two stacks of warehouses of very similar design to those at Albert on 6 September 1852, and by 25 October the building contractor was on site. In his annual reports of both 1853 and 1854, Hartley complains of the lack of progress by Messrs Tomkinson, a firm which had long-standing and generally successful traditions of working for the Dock Committee. The North Stack was completed in September 1854, and its subsequent history is broadly comparable with that of the Albert warehouses: it had the same advantage of security and structural strength, and the same disadvantage of

The barely visible change in gradient of Walter Street is the only shred of evidence left of the original rail connection of Stanley Dock

(Colin Pitcher)

Under these bridges ran the Central Docks' first railway connection; the empty site was that of the LNWR Waterloo Goods Depot. This picture was taken from the show flat in the Waterloo Corn Warehouses

(Colin Pitcher)

standing by the side of a dock with a comparatively small entrance. It should, however, be recognized that the width of the entrance must have seemed reasonable at the time, for the future seemed to lie with the iron screw steamer, and early screw vessels were long and narrow: of those mentioned above as having trouble in Nelson Dock the widest was *Calpe* of 980 registered tons, but only 28 feet wide. It was the next great wave of ship growth in the 1880s, coupled with a trend towards smaller length to beam ratios, which made the entrance to Stanley inadequate, and Hartley can scarcely be criticized for failing to see that far ahead. The obsolescence of the dock must be laid at the door of a later generation which failed to modernize it.

In its early years Stanley had two decisive advantages over Albert. The connection with the Leeds and Liverpool Canal was relatively less important, since the main traffics on the canal were in heavy low-value goods such as coal, flagstones, slates, and pig-iron which obviously did not need the services of high-quality warehousing.[6] Much more important was the connection with the Lancashire and Yorkshire Railway, which enabled direct dispatch of the bonded or high-value goods from the warehouses to most of the key towns of the Lancashire hinterland and beyond. There was also a connection to the Dock Railway, on which Hartley had started work in 1850, progressing gradually year by year until the rails extended from Bankfield Road in the north to Brunswick Dock in the south.[7] This not only provided access from Stanley to other docks, but also to the lines of the London and North Western Railway, and eventually to others as well. It has been customary to mock both Jesse Hartley and the Dock Committee for their resolute refusal to have anything to do with locomotive haulage on the Dock Railway. After all, everyone knows that by 1850 the steam locomotive reigned supreme as the very epitome of the progress of Victorian technology. In common with many popularly held beliefs on the subject of nineteenth-century railways, this view is heavily conditioned by the surprisingly sophisticated marketing methods employed by railway companies to create just such an image. On average, a locomotive on a British railway was available for work four days out of seven and actually hauled a train for something around three hours out of twenty-four on each of those four days. Detailed figures of fuel consumption were not kept by British companies, but the figures available for Belgian railways in 1849 indicate that of 31,920 tons of coke burned, approximately one third (10,674 tons) disappeared in lighting up and in standing waiting in steam.[8] In short, the steam locomotive at this time was highly inefficient both in capital utilization and in fuel economy, and it must be remembered that all of the 10,674 tons consumed at a standstill in Belgium were inserted in fireboxes by footplate crews who were not going anywhere either – but were being paid for it. Such a situation would be acceptable if the locomotive earned its keep during the times it was at work, but in the docks it was most unlikely that it would.

The advantage of the steam locomotive lay in its ability to haul long trains at high speeds, and in 1850 even long-distance mainline freight was only just catching up with passenger traffic in revenue terms. This provides no grounds at all for assuming that it was a suitable prime mover for shunting comparatively modest numbers of decidedly small wagons over short distances. On the contrary, when railway yards and dockside lines employed numerous single-wagon turntables for negotiating corners (there being insufficient space for curves) the locomotive was a bulky and indelicate tool for carrying out hundreds of inch-perfect movements of stock. Furthermore, to get from one siding to another, a locomotive needed to run to and from points or turntables, while a horse could walk directly from one track to another. For movements entirely confined to the yard, the hydraulic capstan became the main competitor to the horse.

The main objection publicly made to the use of locomotives was, of course, that sparks from their chimneys represented an unacceptable fire hazard, an objection which may today seem to savour of over-caution. However, there are to this day only two effective methods of making a steam locomotive work hard without producing such volumes and density of black smoke as to represent not merely a nuisance but a positive danger to traffic. The first of these, the use of high quality hard coal in conjunction with a brick arch and the admission of a little 'top air' could not be applied, largely because the brick arch had not yet been invented. The second was to fire on coke. Because coke produced almost nothing in the way of thermal output from its flue gases, the only way to make lots of steam with it was to use quite wide fire bar spacings and apply a considerable amount of steam blast with a decidedly late cut-off. The practical result of this was that the 'sparks' which were seen as a fire risk were not what we picture as a 'spark' but white hot pieces of coke of half an inch or more across, ejected to a height of 20 feet or so.

It is quite clear from Hartley's comments on the first suggestion for a high level passenger railway that the great need in discharging vessels was to have vehicles available on the quayside to remove cargo as quickly as it emerged from the ship.[9] There was no respect in which the cost and inconvenience of steam locomotives would have helped the attainment of that objective. Speed in haulage would produce only minimal saving of time over the distances of a few hundred yards involved and it would gain it at greatly enhanced risk of accident or fire. The combination of the rail to reduce friction, as in the original colliery tramways, with the simplicity and flexibility of horse haulage was not a failure to come to terms with progress, but a success in choosing the level of technology (and investment) appropriate to the task in hand. Because the Dock Committee tended to be influenced by complaints of delay to ships and rather less so by delay to goods, the secondary benefits of this method of working tend to be neglected, but they were none the less substantial for that. The need for transhipment of goods from road cart to railway wagon was eliminated, the hire of the cart was saved and the control of the whole operation was unified under the officers of the docks. That in turn might even have allowed the rationalization of charges for cartage and porterage, from a situation where a keg of 1 cwt of nails was charged 1d while a cask of hardware was charged 11d as parts of the same consignment from Rabone's of Birmingham to Melbourne.[10] That, however, was too great a benefit to expect.

In September 1850, the Dock Committee received a letter from a group of Lancashire coal owners, requesting a meeting to discuss the possibility of improving facilities for the export of coal from Liverpool. This meeting duly took place on 19 September, and it was agreed that a high level connection with the Lancashire and Yorkshire Railway would be a suitable solution. Following further consultations, Hartley was requested to draw up an outline scheme, which was presented on 7 November and proved sufficiently attractive to prompt a request for detailed plans and estimates after further comings and goings had occupied some ten months. It was not until 7 February 1852 that the detailed scheme was discussed, and although no verbatim notes survive in the minutes, it is clear that members were worried by the estimated cost of £61,500.[11] Such a worry would be understandable, for having completed the five smaller docks in 1848 and Wellington, Sandon and Huskisson in 1851–2 they were now working on Hartley's last and greatest dock, Canada, a monster of 17 acres with an entrance 100 ft wide. At the same time major improvements were proceeding at the south end on Salthouse, Wapping, Queens and Coburg Docks. The collapse of railway construction following on the 1845–7 mania had resulted in a decline in the number of railway navvies from about 257,000 in 1847 to less than 36,000 in 1852,[12] making the labour market easier for Hartley. The ready availability of experienced navvies would not, however, alter the fact that these were huge amounts of capital work to undertake in such rapid succession and the expenditure was a strain even on the 'boomtown' resources of Liverpool at the time.

The first result of the committee's caution was the presentation by William Laird, Secretary of the Wigan Coal Association, of estimates of traffic which the proposed rail link might expect to attract. Taking

The last remains of the lift bridge carrying the high level coal railway over the Dock Road, seen in 1984 – now demolished.

(Author)

the existing markets for coal consumption on the Cheshire side of the river and for export from Liverpool, he assumed a market penetration of 50 per cent, and to that he added 33 per cent of the market for 'river consumption' (mainly bunker coal), which would thus take 100,000 tons. Fifty per cent of the coasting trade, much of which he assumed would be gained from Preston, added another 35,000 tons, and it was assumed that the entire Irish trade and the needs of the Cheshire salt trade would be supplied, adding a further 100,000 tons and making a grand total of 405,000 tons. At a notional charge of 2d per ton, this would yield a revenue of £3,375 p.a. – and an enormous saving on cartage.[13]

The second result was a request to Hartley to produce a cheaper scheme by shortening the railway, stopping it short at the south quay of Bramley-Moore Dock instead of turning down the south quay as originally proposed. This reduced the cost sufficiently to make the project look as though it had a good chance of producing an acceptable return on the capital, and on 18 March 1852 the committee made a site visit, pronounced themselves satisfied, and resolved that the scheme proceed.[14]

There now followed something of an hiatus, and as late as March 1854, little enough work had been done to allow the acceptance by the committee of a deviation proposed by the railway company, bringing the track onto the Dock Estate well to the south of the original location near the Sandon Dock gate. It was reiterated that the bridge across the Dock Road must have a lifting span to allow the passage of large indivisible loads on the road.

Work now proceeded in earnest, and the hydraulic machinery for lifting and tipping the wagons was ordered from Armstrong's in May 1855, the railway being complete and in operation on 23 December 1856. It is clear that its early operation was the source of some confusion: until 27 October 1858, when a superintendent was appointed, the control of its use was haphazard, and even after that there are passing references which make it clear that the division of responsibility between the Board (as it had now become) and the L&YR was often vague at day-to-day operational level. Problems frequently arose through the railway not sending down wagons in sufficient numbers to keep the cranes constantly in work, thus blocking the berths with partly laden vessels, while on the other side, Hartley appears to have underestimated the space required for vessels to discharge ballast before loading coal, causing occasional delays on the railway as coal arrived before the ship was ready to take it. Like other railways within the dock estate, it was horse-hauled, and complaints about the number and quality of horses supplied by L&YR arose, as did occasional rows over coal being sent in wagons other than the correct end-tipping variety. Although for every complaint there were something of the order of 100 working days when nothing went seriously wrong, the impression created is not of a model of efficiency,[15] and the practice of operation fell well short of theoretical capacity.

By the late '60s, the tempo and the stridency of complaints increased, with a continuing crescendo in the '70s, showing a pattern familiar in other overcrowded facilities of the port. There were three broad categories of vessel using the dock: steamers, sea-going sailing vessels, and flats. Owners in each category explained in detail how harmful it was that vessels of the other categories gained preferential treatment, with only occasional outbursts of unity on such issues as the loading of part-cargoes of ballast coal or the supply of bunker coal. Such representations only served to allow members of the

Board to assume that since all parties were complaining more or less equally, the system must be quite fair. They therefore toyed around with trifling expedients like lengthening of working hours during the months when daylight permitted. The eminently intelligent suggestion by the superintendent that the cheapest way to increase capacity was to install 'brilliant lighting' to allow night-time working (which during the winter would have trebled the capacity) could be brushed aside on the grounds that it was made in March – as one might expect on the basis of his experience of chaos during the months of short daylight – and the days would soon be getting longer anyway. October, it would seem, was much too far ahead to be planning. The truth of the matter was probably that, for neither the first nor the last time, the interests of the Central Docks were subordinated to grander schemes elsewhere: the huge programme of works under the 1873 Act was in hand, guzzling money and preoccupying the Works Committee, the engineer and all his staff.

It is extraordinary that there should have been such a dilatory attitude. The coalfields of south Lancashire and north Cheshire were among the great coal producing areas of the world, raising something of the order of 3 million tons per year, of which not much over 10 per cent found its way to export via Liverpool. The London & North Western Railway was investing in its competing facilities for coal export at Garston, yet the Dock Board records give the impression that any minor improvement made was undertaken as an act of charity towards the shippers of coal. Unglamorous as it might be, coal was a valuable market which Liverpool could ill afford to spurn, yet the impression created was that the port was there primarily to engage in the more prestigious long-distance trades. Not until 1869 does it appear that there was any concern about the overcrowding of the berths at Bramley-Moore. On 10 November that year, the Traffic Committee received a report from the Traffic Manager which stated that each of the four cranes could load 1,000 tons per day of twelve hours, and the record total for a month had been 33,881 tons, yet the average over the last year had been only 21,449 tons per month: less than six days' work at the theoretical full capacity. In the Board's book, this was a serious under-use of the facility they provided which could only be accounted for by the fact that the L&YR was not delivering coal at the required rate, and it was stated that for an average of fifty-nine hours per week, one or more cranes were waiting for coal.

The doubling of the track is clearly visible in this view of the approach from Sandhills to the Dock Road. In 1991 this was the last substantial remnant
(Colin Pitcher)

In the Board's view, this was entirely the fault of the railway. The railway argued that there were occasions when they had coal wagons queuing to discharge and the vessels were not there to receive the coal. In these mutual accusations of incompetence the safest judgement appears to be that both were right and each was wrong. It is quite clear from the complaints from ship and flat-owners that the business of making sure that berths were always occupied by vessels seeking to load or actually loading was ill managed, and berths could be found either empty or occupied by vessels which had been loaded and which were still trimming cargo for twenty-four hours or more. Equally, there undoubtedly were occasions when the single track down from Sandhills Station and the sidings serving it were insufficient for the traffic, with the result that ships, cranes and men sat around waiting for coal to arrive. Attempts to make minor improvements to the system, such as the requirement for returns to be made

Coal elevators, loading at the new extension, to bunker ships in the larger docks to the north.

(NMGM)

from Sandhills of the amount of coal available for shipment at 8.00 a.m. and 4.00 p.m. each day met with correspondingly minor success, as did the regulation that no vessel should occupy a berth at the railway unless a specified proportion of its intended cargo was already at Sandhills. The fact was that both the Board and the railway company were only toying with the problem: the high level railway needed to be able to work in concentrated spurts when a vessel was below it, and making facile calculations which allowed nothing for manoeuvring or trimming time could only partly conceal the fact that serious investment was needed in expanding the facilities, possibly even to the extent of enlarging them to the size originally proposed by Jesse Hartley and some might argue that even that was insufficient.

One minor alteration, authorized in March 1871, does appear to have made a definite improvement. A constant source of friction had been that shipowners resented the ability of flats to 'nip in' and load from a crane which was obstructed to larger vessels, thereby often stealing the turn of one of their ships. Obviously they regarded flats with great disdain, but the cargoes the flats carried, for bunkering large steamers in the river or to feed the ever-hungry brine-pans of Cheshire were important ones. The addition of a simple and inexpensive hand tip and shoot at the southern extremity of the railway allowed some measure of separation of ships and flats and made life easier for the crane operators, who had often found the hold of a flat a rather small target at which to aim a whole wagon-load of coal: complaints of coal dropped in the dock were made from time to time, and treated with great seriousness.

The increasing pace at which the railway had to work obviously required that the superintendent was a fairly authoritative character, and it would appear that some, at least, of the complaints which came in were the result of the superintendent being insufficiently forceful in moving vessels on after they had loaded as well as in his working relationships with the railway employees. Accordingly, Ebenezer Owens was removed from the post, not for any misconduct or identifiable incompetence, and found another situation with the Board. His former post was upgraded from his pay rate of about 30 shillings per week to £150 per year, and his successor does seem to have brought about an improvement in throughput. The new record for a day's work set on 23 March the following year was, at 2,357 tons, well up on anything previously achieved, and the figure of 11,576 tons for the same week indicated that sustained improvement was possible. However, these figures, impressive as they were, show that any idea the Board had of achieving the theoretical maximum which could be handled by the cranes would be better forgotten. At the end of the same year, a meeting of members of the coal trade, ungrateful as ever, wrote to the Board 'That in the opinion of this meeting the accommodation provided for the export coal trade is totally inadequate, causing serious loss to all concerned.' If the inadequacy was indeed causing loss to the Board, they certainly were not concerned, for when the engineer reported on possible extension of the high level railway to the Works Committee on 10 March 1876 they agreed they 'cannot recommend the outlay'. Perhaps this failure to invest was intended as a christening present for the new North Dock at Garston, with its four coal drops connected to the large system of sidings already built there by the largest railway company in the country, which was just nearing completion.

The next three years saw a number of accidents caused by failure of lifting tackle, mostly the cradle chains which supported the wagons.[16]

Unfortunately the engineer's reports of his investigations into the causes have not survived, but whatever the particular cause, the general cause is perfectly clear: the railway and its equipment were being overworked. The Works Committee clearly suspected that the railway company was easing its congestion problems by overloading wagons, but equally it is clear that insufficient down-time was allowed on the cranes and it is probable that the necessary periodic annealing of the wrought iron lifting chains was neglected. The readiness with which the Board agreed to meet several small claims for damage caused to vessels in this way is an indication that they knew that undue pressure was leading to unsafe working practices. Happily, it appears that no crewmen or Board employees were injured in these accidents. In October 1879 the engineer was instructed to strengthen the cranes by unspecified means at a total cost of £200, and the following April a brand new 23-ton crane was ordered, followed by two more in July. It is interesting to note in passing that this latter order appears to have been one of the fruits of Harold Littledale's agitation against the practice of ordering all hydraulic machinery from Armstrong's: it was the Board's first order to E.B. Ellington's Hydraulic Engineering Company at Chester. He would have been wise to deliver by the agreed date: his delay let Armstrong's back in.

Before this new equipment had been installed, the Works Committee at last decided that the railway as built was too small and must be extended, on condition that the railway company doubled the line down from Sandhills, to enable the flow of wagons to meet the enhanced loading capacity. This condition was readily agreed, as well it might be, when the L&YR had endured ten years' competition from the LNWR, who in 1870 had gained access for Wigan as well as St Helens, with coal to Garston. Across the river at Birkenhead the coal exports, mainly from the GWR, were running at three times the level of the Liverpool trade. As early as 1866, the GWR had been routing 8.6 per cent of their total long-haul coal trade through Birkenhead, and their access to the Welsh Valleys as well as to the West Midlands and the Wrexham Coalfields made them formidable competitors. The Board had good grounds for making the condition: they were concerned about the large and growing measure of control over freight traffic nationwide which was being exercised by a small number of large railway companies which might act in concert and which were given to merging, or to leasing each other, to enhance that control. In 1872, the Board had been among the objectors to a bill for the amalgamation of the LNWR with the L&YR: had the objectors not carried the day the consequence might well have been the centralization of coal export from the whole of the Lancashire coalfield at the railway-owned ports of Garston and Fleetwood.[17]

The Board's caution would be strengthened by the fact that all the canals which might bring coal to the Mersey (principally the Leeds & Liverpool, the Bridgewater and the St Helens Canal) were effectively controlled by railway interests. Even the Shropshire Union Canal, which would be a rather desperate way of bringing coal from Staffordshire, was controlled by the LNWR.[18] A desire to see some extra financial commitment from the railway company was, therefore, a sensible and indeed necessary protection of their own investment in extra plant and construction.

The Works Committee approval of the scheme was on 25 May 1880, and what they approved was very like the original plan of Jesse Hartley before its reduction, except that Lyster's extension ran along the north side of Bramley-Moore instead of the south. It was to be

The original portion of the high level coal railway

(NMGM)

some 400 feet long, equipped with two cranes and would take ten to twelve months to complete at an estimated cost of £26,000. This figure seemed wildly optimistic as soon as the order was placed with the Teesside Iron & Engine Works Co. Ltd, for the wrought ironwork (only): this was estimated at 1,572 tons at £11 per ton.[19] There is no record of any second thoughts having troubled the Board or the Works Committee, but figures were compiled for a report on the extent and profitability of the traffic in the year ending 31 December 1880. These show a total of 410,558 tons of coal shipped, of which 126,669 tons went overseas and 97,868 coastwise, producing dues income of £2,531. The considerable balance (over 186,000 tons) was divided between coal delivered directly into bunkers and that loaded into flats for river traffic, much of which would also find its way into bunkers of ships anchored in the river. This bunkering traffic is the reason for the high level coal railway appearing at first glance to return rather slender profits on the considerable investment involved, but at a date when sailing tonnage was dwindling both in extent and importance, it was a vital service upon which depended much of the general revenue of the port. The seemingly lukewarm enthusiasm of the Board for Bramley-Moore can, however, be put into perspective by recalling that over the same period the Birkenhead coal berths shifted no less than 1,377,658 tons, and also returned much better-looking profits on paper.[20]

The starting of the work in August 1881 was marked by some lack of urgency, since Lamport & Holt continued to use their appropriated berth at the East End, north side, presumably where the works must begin, until September 1881, when they were moved to the berth directly opposite, on the south side. Meanwhile, the improvement of the old section was still proceeding. On 13 February 1882 it was reported that SS *Craigmore* had successfully loaded the first nocturnal cargo of coal and that the new gas lighting was found to be sufficient in every respect. The cost of this improvement, undertaken after some consideration of the merits of the new technology of electric lighting, had only been £250 and it remains hard to explain why such an inexpensive method of increasing potential throughput had not been implemented years previously.

On 6 July 1882, the Board confirmed a recommendation that the order for the new cranes, now increased to five in number, should be placed with Armstrong's at a total cost of £12,400. This item and the

Remains of the original section along East Wellington, during demolition, July 1991. The photographer was standing on the remains of the new extension
(Colin Pitcher)

ironwork took the cost £3,600 over budget before a brick had been bought, much less laid, and matters were yet to deteriorate, for on 17 November Lyster informed the Works Committee that the capacity of the pumping plant was insufficient to meet the consumption of the new cranes and would require the purchase and installation of an additional engine and accumulator at a cost of £7,300. It is difficult to understand how such a miscalculation could have come about. Unlike steam or compressed air, water is inelastic, and the volume of water required to work a crane or other similar appliance is a simple matter of the volume of the ram multiplied by the maximum duty cycle (i.e. frequency of operation) which results in a figure of gallons per minute. That figure is unaffected by the load condition or any other variable, and when multiplied by a rule of thumb figure for the mechanical efficiency for the pumps, which at this date was around 75 per cent, is directly related to a required number of horsepower to drive the system. The power for the existing portion of the railway came from the ageing pumping station at Stanley Dock, but the new engine was to work on its own, serving only the high level railway and in all normal circumstances meeting the entire demand. It was a twin tandem compound engine of 230 hp, very similar to the well-known preserved engines of Tower Bridge. The need for such a powerful machine, which would deliver over 170 net horsepower into the mains, indicates that the Stanley system was already overloaded before the extension to the railway was determined upon and that overload must have been a significant factor in the shortfall of coal shipped as compared with the theoretical shipping capacity of the cranes. Yet no mention of power supply had been made during the lengthy discussions of the Board or its committees in the lead up to the decision to build the extension. Even when the engine was ordered, no mention was made of a building in which to put it or of boilers to supply it with steam. The machinery was in fact housed for the most part in the first two arches of the new length of viaduct, with the addition of the very handsome accumulator house and chimney which still stand. In December 1882 an order was sent to Daniel Adamson & Co. for a pair of Lancashire boilers at an estimated cost of £825.

If the decision-making had been affected by a lack of complete and relevant information presented to Board members, it must be added that the project management surpassed it in inadequacy. From an estimate of £26,000 and ten to twelve months, it progressed bit by bit to a final completion in thirty-eight months at a cost of £83,927. It would be unfair to attribute this astonishing performance entirely to the engineer however, for since the 'go ahead' was received in May 1880 the new extension had grown in length from 400 to 908 feet, which of course scaled up all the costs proportionately.[21] Two cranes, for example, became five. However, by a crude measurement of cost per foot run, these additions should still have resulted in a cost only in the region of £60,000. The real significance of the overspend, however, is that it was of sufficient magnitude to make nonsense of the calculations on which the decision of May 1880 had been based. The decision had become a gamble on considerable future expansion in traffic, with no indications as to whether or not there would be any revenue return on the investment.

The men who were demolishing the extension while the photographer was standing on it kindly provided this sectional view of its construction

(Colin Pitcher)

The new extension was constructed on similar principles to the original section, with massive wrought iron box beams 61 ft long spanning the brick piers and supporting longitudinals onto which the corrugated plate decking was secured.[22] The working surface was of small blocks of greenheart set in asphalt. The old section had been worked with horses to move the wagons, which necessitated longitudinal sleepers to provide a pathway for the horses, but the new section was equipped with hydraulic capstans for shunting and conventional sleepers were employed. However, being a railway shunter was an exceptionally dangerous occupation (in 1888, for example, 77 were killed nationwide and 1,152 seriously injured)[23] and it was determined that a flat working surface was desirable. The rails were, therefore, laid on a second layer of longitudinal sleepers and ballast, surfaced off with woodblocks and tar was applied to cover the cross sleepers to within three inches of the top of the longitudinal ones. The new structure was intended to carry wagons of up to 20 tons as against the 15 ton maximum for the old section, which was strengthened in 1886 for the same weight. Great play was made in the Engineer's Report for 1887 of the fact that it was now possible to use locomotives of up to 20 tons on the high level railway. The liberal provision of capstans had in fact made this capability unnecessary, and it does not appear that locomotives were ever used there.

As on the old section, there were four roads connected by turntables at each crane, but the cranes were made with a large enough reach (37 ft) that when handling 'boxes' they could pick them from wagons on any except the furthest road. Each crane had distinct sets of rams and chains for lifting or lowering, and for tipping. The end-tipping wagons were lifted in a cradle and swung out over the vessel and then both rams were allowed to exhaust water, lowering the cradle on an even keel. When it had reached the desired height, the tipping ram valve was closed while the lifting ram continued to lower, thus tipping the cradle and wagon together and causing the coal to fall. If necessary, the tipping ram could then be raised a little to increase the inclination and dislodge any coal stuck in the bottom of the wagon. Boxes were emptied in a similar way: each box had two sets of lifting chains and when weight was transferred from the set attached to the lifting ram onto those on the tipping ram the bottom doors opened and the coal fell.

Theoretically, these machines could work pretty rapidly, tipping up to about 300 tons per hour each, or 1,500 tons per hour with all five working. In practice, for a variety of reasons, this figure was never even approached. Many ships did not have hatches large enough to receive coal at 300 tons per hour without frequent pauses for trimming and the logistics of delivering a full wagon to every crane and removing an empty one every two minutes were beyond the rail side of the operation, probably through lack of siding space. To enable ships of varying length and hatch disposition to be reasonably sure of being able to come straight to a crane, the cranes were placed closer together than would otherwise be necessary, with the result that it was very rare for all of them to work at once. Taking these factors together, the average rate of tipping on the whole of the new extension was only of the order of 200 tons per hour and the old portion of the railway averaged 322 tons per appliance per *day* over 1883–4. The rather ludicrous situation existed that the hand tip, which had been put in to prevent grubby little flats from delaying the serious ships, was in fact far faster than the cranes. This machine consisted of a cradle which held the wagon and which was tilted off-balance by a hand operated crab winch. Gravity being on its side, it then tipped the rest of the way on its own, restrained by a brake. Once the weight of coal had gone, the counterweight brought the empty wagon back up. This much simpler machine was capable of dealing with wagons at a rate of more than one per minute, or double the rate of the inherently much more complicated cranes. Its disadvantages were that greater breakage of the coal occurred and it was, of course, only able to tip into vessels small enough to get below its 'shoots'. Because the flats were so much easier to move on and off the berth, the average rates of loading over a period were even more favourable to the hand tip.

It appears that what was really wrong with the high level coal railway is that the members had never really started from square one and decided what it was for. They wanted the coal trade, and they wanted to keep the coal owners happy, but they were never clear in their own minds as to whether they were providing a revenue earning service for coal export or whether they were providing a facility for steamship owners in the shape of a convenient and inexpensive bunkering service. At first sight it might appear that in either case the problem was merely to get as much coal into vessels as quickly and cheaply as possible. The reality was that the right answer could only emerge as a response to a question, and the question was unclear. In the circumstances, the new stretch of high level must be considered to have acquitted itself quite honourably, as it increased its share of the total coal handling of the port, reaching about 30 per cent soon after opening. It handled almost all of the coastal trade, but only about 20 per cent of the bunkering, the rest of the latter being provided from Birkenhead. The dominance of Birkenhead in that market was not entirely the result of any failing at Bramley-Moore: it arose from the fact that the masters and owners of many vessels wanted good hard steam coal in their bunkers, which gave more miles per ton, and the very best steam coal came from the Welsh valleys on the Great Western Railway to Birkenhead. Lancashire steam coal was by comparison rather soft and sooty stuff and thus more expensive to use in bunkers where every ton of coal carried was a ton of payload lost.[24]

If it is legitimate to suggest a lack of clarity in the Board's objectives, it must also be admitted that the coal handling situation was really much more complex than the simple figures quoted suggest. It is well known that some owners and masters preferred to take on coal using the ship's own tackle, working overside from canal boats. This may have been relatively slow, but it was cheap, made the cargo easier to trim and saved the hassle of queuing to get a berth at the coaling appliances. The exact amounts shipped this way are impossible to discover, but between 1855 and 1858 the amount of coal coming to Liverpool by canal increased from 765,065 tons to 1,205,588 tons.[25] Much of that, of course, was bound for local domestic and industrial consumption, but the increase was substantially more than the total amount taken by the new competitor at Bramley-Moore. A further complication is the amount of coal which was actually consumed on the Dock Estate. By 1890 the coaling appliances at Bramley-Moore themselves consumed well over 1,000 tons per year, Waterloo Corn Warehouses used nearly 2,000 and the new impounding stations around 3,000 each. Major improvement works, such as those at Canada in the early 1890s required huge amounts fed into large numbers of fairly small and inefficient boilers on cranes, steam navvies and other plant to the extent of about 5,000 tons per year at that site alone. Because coal prices often fluctuated wildly, the Board purchased its own coal from a variety of areas. At the turn of the century, for example, it was buying quite large amounts of Staffordshire coal,[26] and there is no reason to assume that shippers of coal were any less flexible in their search for the right coal at the right price. The place of origin of the coal would affect the point of arrival at the Dock Estate, which might, in turn, affect the competitive position of Bramley-Moore as against, say, Herculaneum. From the records which survive, it appears that the Board did not really attempt to disentangle the figures for coal movement in any detail, and when tonnage figures kept rising they had every encouragement not to make their brains hurt. What is, perhaps, surprising, is that they did not notice the declining share of the total coal shipment market which they were supplying,[27] yet it appears that the first expressions of concern were not made until the total market itself declined, leading to dramatic falls in traffic at Bramley-Moore in the early 1930s. By the time it was noted, the decline was terminal: the continuing rise in the average size of ships and the sinking proportion of them burning coal coupled with a marked decline in the export market led to a fall in traffic of 34.86 per cent over the five years ending 1 July 1934. The desire to get coal to very large vessels had already led to a successful experiment at Gladstone No. 1 branch in 1927 when SS *Ascanius* was coaled using an ordinary quayside crane but an even more bitter blow for Bramley-Moore was the arrival of imported coal. Most of this was coastal, including most of the supply for the new Clarence Dock Power Station, but in 1936 SS *Scholar* brought in 4,700 tons of German coal for bunkering Harrison liners.

The outbreak of the Second World War, and the need to coal anything that would float (to say nothing of the recovery of Harrisons' business) meant that the high level railway was again in great demand, and appliances which had been laid up were hastily recommissioned. This, of course, could not last long after the war, and as early as November 1945 there began a spiral of rising costs and falling demand which could have only one end. By 1964 the cost of dropping coal had risen from its wartime level of 7½d per ton to 2s 1d and on 8 October 1966 the Board confirmed the recommendation to close it down. In its 110 years of operation, nothing about it had changed radically. The hydraulic pumps, which in 1911 had been reconnected to the rest of the system, continued in service as the main supply for the central area until that too was abandoned.

CHAPTER FIVE

NEW TRAFFIC, BUT THE SAME OLD STORY

If, however, nothing much had changed on the high level railway, there had been one important development underneath it. The passage of the Contagious Diseases (Animals) Act in 1878 had resulted in the centralization of livestock imports from many countries being landed at designated Foreign Animals Wharves, only those from countries considered to be free of disease continuing to be landed at the Central Docks. One man who was landing Irish cattle there was an Irish butcher called James Nelson, and his business appears to have prospered to such an extent that he began to encounter problems in acquiring sufficient cattle to meet the demand. Considerable strides had recently been made in the theory and practice of refrigeration from the time of the world's first meat-freezing factory which opened in Australia in 1866 to the point where the machinery was sufficiently cheap and reliable to bring to birth the public ice skating rink. At a more serious commercial level, it had been established that ocean voyages carrying refrigerated cargo were technically possible. Enterprising men like James Nelson and his sons, Hugh and William, put these facts together and arrived at the answer of the Nelsons River Plate Meat Company.[1] There being no public cold store available on the Dock Estate at the time, they decided to construct their own, and in late 1884 they negotiated a lease of the westernmost arch of the high level coal railway extension for a period of three years and obtained the consent of the Board to start work on converting it into a cold store before the start date of the lease, which was 1 January 1885. They proceeded with great urgency; the evening of 31 December, for example, being spent not in festivities but in laying the floor. By 25 February the arch had been converted and was ready for cargo. It was obviously a little rough and ready, for the hydraulic pipework serving the coaling cranes still ran along the ceiling, causing problems with condensation dripping in the boiler house and compressor room and occasional leakage onto the stored meat. As well as suffering nuisance, they created it, and on 20 January 1886, HM Customs evacuated their building which stood immediately to the west of the arch on the grounds that it had been made uninhabitable by the heat and noise from Nelsons' machinery. Given that Nelsons' business was doing extremely well and that they rented another arch and the Customs building as well shortly afterwards, one is tempted to wonder how accidental the nuisance may have been. Perhaps more surprising than these nuisances which occurred is the one which did not: there was never any complaint made of meat, or indeed Nelsons' employees, suffering from the clouds of dust which rose when coal was being tipped.

The cold store being directly under No. 9 crane, there was obviously no question of an appropriated berth on the Bramley-Moore side. Across the avenue lay Wellington Half-Tide Dock: although this was to be extensively remodelled in a programme begun in 1902 which did away with the tiresome tidal basin at Sandon, its south quay stood then as it remains today. The berth was not formally appropriated to Nelsons', but was apparently more or less so on a 'nod and a wink' basis with the harbourmaster. There was good access to the dock railway, the Board making minor improvements at the outset and rather more ambitious ones as the success of Nelsons' business became apparent. A third arch was added, but it is also clear that some meat was being consigned directly by rail, as the Board provided four large movable stagings to facilitate discharge from ship to train.[2]

The Nelson business was not the only successful venture: the Vestey brothers were also prospering in the frozen meat trade, though not, it would appear, quite so rapidly. In 1890, Nelson formed the first of a series of single-ship companies, the *Highland Scot* Steamship Company, followed the same year by *Highland Chief*, and in 1891 by three more vessels. In 1898 the single-ship companies were wound up to form Nelson Line (Liverpool) Ltd. It was perhaps the last boom trade involving large ocean tonnages to appear 'out of the blue' as the result of a technical innovation, and it grew with spectacular rapidity. The secret of its success was partly a social factor in the market place: this was the time when the upper working class was becoming richer, and was using its new-found wealth to adopt middle-class values, a tendency manifest in, for example, the fashion for keeping a 'best room' in a terraced house. Argentine beef was not as good as home grown, especially in the early days of the trade, as the freezing process tended to dry it out, but it was much cheaper and readily obtainable.[3] It enabled the better-off working class family to adopt the middle-class practice of a roast joint for Sunday dinner, and thus opened up a huge new market. Between 1888 and 1913, Britain's per capita consumption of meat doubled. In 1880 Argentina had produced 3,571 carcasses for export and in 1900 this had risen to 2,332,837. Yet the Dock Board had stoutly resisted applications to build large cold stores at various sites in the North Docks, and converted railway arches remained the only accessible accommodation for nearly twenty years, until Union Cold Storage finally managed to gain approval for their large new building at Alexandra. Whether this was a misguided attempt to protect the livestock trade at Woodside, or simply because the Board failed to realize what they were missing is unclear, but the result was that Nelsons' soldiered on in their railway arches until 1923, when an attempt at raising their rent for the use of obsolescent facilities by a factor of nearly three times, led to their departure, completed in 1927. The greater part of their trade was lost to London.

The Liverpool Overhead Railway had originally been envisaged as a steam-hauled railway, though the obvious fire risk from steam locomotives had given rise to consideration of both cable haulage (which had been much improved by the developers of street cable-cars) and pneumatic power (which was highly desirable, but of low efficiency). The lengthy delays in construction of the railway allowed sufficient time for electric traction to emerge as a serious possibility, and when it became clear that, in addition to its other advantages of safety and cleanliness, electric traction would allow a saving on the structure greater than the extra costs of the stock and the generating plant, the decision was taken to adopt the new technology. That meant finding a location for a generating station which must meet three requirements. To equalize voltage drop, it needed to be about half-way along the route; to feed its condensers there must be a cheap and plentiful supply of water; and it must have reasonable access to coal supplies. These requirements were met by the unoccupied arches under the old portion of the high level railway.[4] The company's application for a lease passed around the Committees of Works, Traffic and Docks and Quays before the Board finally approved a lease of twenty-one years at £750 per year,[5] of the southernmost two arches. The procedure was quite a ponderous one, and its completion within only thirteen days from the receipt of the railway company's enquiry indicated considerable goodwill on the part of the Board and its officers.

A month later, the company was back again, asking for a small patch of land to the south of their arches, on which to erect a chimney and the economizers. They also sought permission to make openings in the dock wall for the abstraction and return of condenser water, and to make hatchways in the deck of the high level railway to allow coal to be tipped directly to the boiler house. All these were granted, as were requests for the use of some other small pieces of land adjacent which were not, in the end, taken up.

The railway, having taken the bold decision to employ electric traction, did not feel inclined to take chances with innovative generating plant, and installed machines driven by the tried and tested method of the slow-speed mill engine with multiple rope drive. These required a great deal of space, and could not really compete in thermal or mechanical efficiency with the high-speed direct coupled generating engines developed by Willans or Belliss and Morcom, but it was still found that less space was needed than had been anticipated, and in August 1893 the Board agreed to take back 651 square yards which were surplus to requirements and to reduce the rent pro rata. By 1895, the railway was looking for extra space again to increase the capacity of the generating station, installing one extra set and a new control board to meet the needs of the extensions to the original route.

The generating plant had been designed with reliability as its most important quality. It certainly appears that thermal efficiency came rather lower down, as in 1897 the Works Committee was informed of the engineer's concern that heat from the boiler house was damaging the decking of the high level railway. This was happening fifty years after the best Cornish engineers had succeeded in keeping the air temperatures of their engine and boiler houses only a few degrees above ambient. It is, therefore, scarcely surprising that as generating plant improved, power stations became first large and then huge; the price of coal rose, the Overhead Railway's generating station became too expensive to run, and in 1926, following on considerable investment by Liverpool Corporation in its municipal supply system, the generating station at Bramley-Moore was closed down.

With the exceptions of the two sides of the Bramley-Moore Dock occupied by the high level railway, and of the Stanley Dock with its lofty warehouses, the whole of the rest of the quays of the 1848 group of docks lasted until 1900 without any significant alteration. Given that virtually every dock to the north of Bramley-Moore and to the south of Albert was either built new or modernized almost out of recognition between 1850 and 1905, some explanation is needed for this absence of modernization.

Although, as mentioned above, the intention in building this group of docks was questioned by the protagonists of Birkenhead, they were in great demand with shipowners right from the start. Appropriated berths at their quays were being sought even before the sheds were built, as in the case of T. Martin and Burns & Co., who sought a berth for their vessels trading to Ireland at South East Nelson, on 27 September 1848. By 1861, despite the proximity of the Sandon and Clarence entrances, severe congestion was being encountered at the Salisbury entrance, resulting in the production of a report by the harbourmaster, supported by another from the dockmaster at Clarence, on means of mitigating the problem. The gates of the entrance were to be opened as early as possible (at the discretion of the dockmaster) and Collingwood, Clarence, Clarence half-tide and Trafalgar were all to be levelled with the tide. The bell in the Victoria Tower was to be rung when the gates were open, and from then until one hour before the top of the tide, traffic was outwards only. The bell was then to be rung again, indicating the beginning of one-way traffic inwards. Any outward-bound vessel which had not made good its exit by the second bell had to wait and attempt to exit after all the inward-bound vessels were safely inside.[6] Such an arrangement would minimize the risk of (frequent) minor collisions, quayside fisticuffs, protests to the Board and attempts to gain precedence by bribing gatemen, piermasters and the like. (The receipt of such bribes had been made an instant dismissal offence for employees of the Dock Committee as early as 22 December 1836, which suggests that there was nothing new about congestion at entrances.) There remained the risk of outward-bound vessels taking their chance on the ebb, which could lead to consequences such as those that befell the *J.C. Boynton* at Princes half-tide entrance in 1871. At 9.00 a.m. on 28 February, her master pushed his luck on the ebb, and grounded on the sill. The ship was badly injured, and filled with water. She was partly unloaded over the next three days, and was finally refloated on 4 March.[7] There could be little doubt that attempts to sail at the last moment on the ebb were unwise, but neither could it be claimed that a system which forced skippers to take this risk was exactly a leader in the increasingly competitive market for the provision of port services.

What lay at the root of the problem was glamour. Top in the glamour stakes, by a long way, came the express passenger liners. They were fast, expensive, and looked very pretty. Then there were the ocean-going cargo liners: because they were expensive to build and to run, they were almost invariably owned or managed by quite substantial companies. In this social scale one had to descend somewhere below the lifeboat of the harbourmaster's launch before arriving at the short sea cargo vessels and then, finally, the untouchable coasters. It may even be worth continuing the metaphor: the passenger liners provided services for the noble and for those who were so rich and influential that they had to be treated as quasi-noble (even if they were utterly crass parvenus). They could, therefore, be considered a sort of equivalent of the butler. The coaster, on the other hand, was fulfilling the social role of the boy who shovelled the muck out of the carriage stables. Now it is well known that no snobbery could match that displayed by the upper servant to the lower, and that is why the Dock Board, dominated as it was by representatives of the glamour trades, exhibited such contempt for the coaster. The butler's worn-out suit was a favour for which the stable boy should wring his cap, whether it fitted him or not, and so it was with dock accommodation for the coaster: if it was more or less big enough it was certainly good enough.

During the reign of Queen Victoria, coasting tonnage increased by roughly 300 per cent. It has been argued that it was quantitatively more important during that period than both railway and canals put together, measuring its contribution to the economy by ton-miles of work performed. Taken purely in tonnage terms alone, it was a market worthy of consideration by any provider of port services.[8]

Trafalgar Dock in the 1920s. Facilities like these were less than ideal by 1860 (NMGM)

There was another, and more important reason, why it should have been taken very seriously indeed. The Dock Board, like other large port authorities, was worried about the growing power of major railway companies, and the mounting evidence that they could and would use this power to distort normal market pressures on a nationwide basis to their own advantage. The evidence that such worries were justifiable has become clear in the last twenty years or so, as economic historians have uncovered machinations which were either hidden from or not understood by those outside the railway industry.[9] As competitors to the power of the railway companies, the canals were totally insignificant (and many of them were under railway control anyway) and the roads were probably worse. The only effective restraint on the power of the railways was the competition of a strong coasting industry. For so long as the coasting industry was expected to operate using facilities originally intended for use by ocean-going ships, but now outgrown by them, it would be reduced in effectiveness.

Owners of coasters had invested heavily in new steam vessels – steam tonnage exceeded sail before 1870 – and their return on this investment came from larger carrying capacity and the capability of making more voyages per year. Yet the berths they had to use in the second port of the country were generally allocated not on the basis of what the ships needed, discharging equipment, well-lighted capacious sheds with large doorways and smooth floors for example, but on what they did not need, such as great depths of water and wide entrance passages. As late as 1897, the Board minuted the acknowledgement of yet more complaints from the coasting trade about the inadequate nature of the berths allocated. Their response was to remark that the coasting trade had recently been allowed to move into Princes Dock, which had formerly been used by foreign vessels.[10] This dock had an entrance with 'haunches' so extensive that they virtually formed an invert arch. All of its shed space was of 1840s style, although the open shed on the west side had been reconstructed as recently as 1872. Only one side of the dock was railway connected; there were no hydraulic lifting appliances and even the supply of mooring bollards was fairly sparse, vessels frequently mooring to shed columns or anything else that looked immobile. The dock was, in short, useless for the ocean traffic for which it had been built and had become so for the longer sea traffics as well.[11] So far from being a generous act on the part of the Board, it was an exploitation of the fact that pressure for coastal berths was so intense that even this was better than nothing. The Board was thus able to gain continued income from a dock which was so outdated that it needed either extensive modernization or abandonment and infilling. On 30 December 1897 the Liverpool & District Millers Association was so ungrateful as to write complaining that facilities for coastal vessels were still 'utterly inadequate . . . more particularly as to the sheds'. The courteously unhelpful reply they received indicates that the Board did not regard this as a matter of great consequence. In view of the fact that the previous year had seen over 25,000 coastal vessels with a total register tonnage of over 4.5 million enter or leave the port with cargoes (i.e. excluding empty or ballasted vessels),[12] that attitude is hard to explain.

There was a further difficulty in the way of the coasting trade. The services the coasters provided, often to areas where the railway system was poor, such as west Wales and large areas of Scotland, were not necessarily for single commodity cargoes such as coal, salt or flour being 'exported' from Liverpool. Many of the cargoes were mixed and the function was a distributive one. Jesse Hartley had been aware that distribution was (and is) a function at the very heart of successful port operation,[13] but his wisdom was soon forgotten as coasters were gathered into ghettos of obsolete docks. This virtually precluded any question of ocean-going vessels discharging overside directly into coasters except in the grain trade. Few of the coastal berths were rail connected, with the result that such cargo was once again at the mercy of the ubiquitous carter, to take its chance in penny lots on the congested and ill-surfaced avenues and quays. The carter's interests may have been well served, but the expense, delay and cluttering of quays and sheds which resulted helped no one else, and the process was, of course, repeated in reverse when coasters arrived bringing goods for export overseas. The Board had, once again, failed to perceive that moving goods, not ships, generates wealth.

The longer sea traders fared better than the coasters, but not very much better. The sheds at Nelson Dock, for example, were not fitted with weatherboarding until 1854. Donald Currie's considerable Hamburg trade was carried on from an open shed at the south-west corner of the dock until 1876, when three bays of it were bricked in, and minor improvements to the lighting and the floor surfaces were made. In 1880 a wooden shed, 180 ft x 36 ft was added, but it took another three years to get stone truckways laid between the two and continuous sliding doors were not fitted to the west shed until 1897. The West India & Pacific Steamship Co. seems to have been better served (or less demanding) at their shed in the north-east corner; once they had got their railway connection improved they seem to have continued happily enough until the increasing size of their vessels caused them to move to Sandon in 1882. W.H. Stott & Co., who managed a string of single-ship companies trading mainly to the Baltic and the Mediterranean, moved in briefly in 1904 but were not impressed with the facilities (although none of their ships exceeded 1,000 tons) and moved back to south side, Bramley-Moore. Latterly, of course, Nelson was largely used by the coasting trade: in 1913 we find that the City of Dublin Steam Packet Co. had been lowering the tone, the Docks and Quays Committee requiring them 'to arrange for the manure from their steamers to be put into vehicles and removed

Observe the prodigal expenditure on quayside lighting: one gas lamp in 250 yards. Docks like these were not, as was claimed, suitable for coasters: they were merely less unsuitable than for ships which could not get into them at all

(NMGM)

direct from the vessels instead of being deposited at the east side of their berth, as is now done'. The demise of Nelson Dock in recognizable form was largely completed in 1965, when Coast Lines were operating container services there, and were allowed to demolish sheds to provide container standing space.

Standards were obviously lower at Collingwood, for the Dundalk & Newry SS Co. were not required to remove the manure from their vessels by cart: on the contrary, they were specifically permitted to build a structure outside their shed at the north side of the dock for its reception whence it was sold and removed by canal. For many years the dock was mainly used by the Irish trade, including The Limerick SP Co., Drogheda SP Co., Sligo SN Co., and a considerable number of vessels for which Thompson, Tedcastle & Co. were agents. The last-named company operated to a variety of destinations, including a twice weekly (increased to three times in 1882) service to Dublin. Just as Currie's had to argue their case for effecting improvements to the obsolete features of their berth, so Thompson Tedcastle had to ask the Docks and Quays Committee for asphalt truckways in their shed in 1876 and three lamps in 1877. They also operated a service to Maryport & Whitehaven from a berth at Clarence half-tide, and in 1882 they asked for a berth at Nelson with a view to transferring both services there. Mere Irish boats were not, of course, important enough to use Nelson Dock at that date, and they had to wait until 9 December 1891. In 1883 they had gained the use of a wooden shed 58 ft x 55 ft infilling the open corner between their two old sheds. At the opposite corner of the dock was a berth for the flats operated by the Shropshire Union Railway & Canal Company, which brought manufactured goods from the Midlands via Ellesmere Port for export, but also provided a transfer service from the large LNWR depot at Egerton Dock and occasionally from Garston as well. This tiny outpost of the mighty LNWR empire (which controlled SURC Co.) was served by a wooden shed 57 ft x 25 ft. The piecemeal nature of these alterations, usually carried out only after extensive discussion, was such that the dock remained a hotch-potch of obsolete or obsolescent little buildings often devoid of the most basic facilities. When, for example, the Bishop's Wharf Carrying Co. was granted a berth on the south side, formerly occupied by the Sligo SN Co., the Docks and Quays Committee agreed that 'it will be necessary for the road side of the sheds at the south side of the Collingwood Dock to be filled in with boarding and slide doors . . .' The clear implication of this resolution is that the shed was, up to that time, one of Jesse Hartley's standard open sheds. The date was 26 March 1930.[14]

CHAPTER SIX

MATTERS OF MOMENT

The members of the Mersey Docks and Harbour Board were important men. They were large scale shipowners like Guion or Brocklebank, shipbuilders like Laird or substantial merchants like Hubback or Littledale. They gave their time on Board business on a completely voluntary basis, for which the only direct reward they received was the recognition and status which came with membership.

The time spent by members in meetings or in reading papers or drafting comments before meetings was not, therefore, a direct cost in hard cash to the port. On the other hand, there was a limit to the amount of time which even the most conscientious member was willing to spend on Board business, so that there was a calculable maximum amount of members' time per week available. Because these were men of considerable commercial substance it must inevitably have been assumed that the Board must profit from their collective wisdom, acumen and experience. That was why it existed. Because the time available was finite, so too was the opportunity of utilizing the asset represented by the attributes of the members of the Board, and therefore one would expect that the normal common-sensical practices which the members themselves adopted for their own businesses would apply to the proceedings of the Board and its committee. Such practices would obviously include the preparation of clear and balanced reports for members' consideration which reduced problems to a logical sequence of simple issues, and the delegation of trivial matters to the lowest trustworthy level. That was how to maximize the usefulness of the resource of members' time, and while the language used in this paragraph is alien to late nineteenth-century business practice, the ideas it expresses certainly are not.

What actually happened was rather different. Much of the series of rows precipitated by Harold Littledale may be characterized by the absence of necessary and accurate information at Board meetings, and Littledale, for one, was not going to be easily convinced that this absence was accidental. When the Works Committee was told, and accepted, that details of the wages paid in the Engineer's Department were not available, they were being deceived in a deliberate manner.[1] Since 1868, the Engineer's Department had kept a series of enormous ledgers entitled 'Total Cost of Works' and any reader who wishes to know how much the men who cleared the ashpits in the boilerhouse at Waterloo Corn Warehouses were paid in a specific week in 1870 can find it faithfully recorded there, along with the cost of any stores the men used and any contract services which had to be engaged on their behalf. The Engineer's Department operated a large and extremely complicated bureaucracy which, after the manner of such bodies, indulged in the compulsive hoarding of information.[2] Vast amounts of information were fed in at great expense: the problem arose when it came to getting any of it out again to form a sensible basis for decision or policy making on the part of the Board or its committees.

The obvious and readily available form in which this huge bulk of information was summarized and supposedly rendered comprehensible and useful was the annual Engineer's Report. These documents are a very useful historical source (and extensive use of them has been made in this and other similar works) but as a working document for the members they left a great deal to be desired. In the first place they were inevitably out of date to a greater or lesser degree, yet they might well be the first intimation that a member of the Works Committee received of a considerable overspend on a project.[3] It was, of course, then too late to do anything constructive about it. A greater difficulty was the way in which expenditure was lumped together, so that a figure of £257,114 19s 1d was given for the improvements at Herculaneum Dock.[4] No breakdown was given of that expenditure, and even with a good deal of painstaking homework through back copies of minutes, it was most unlikely that a member would be able to discover what had been spent on materials, stores, direct labour, contract work, design costs and general overheads. In short, he was unable to form any impression of how well the department was performing. If he had attempted to get information in the shape of a report to the committee, he would probably be voted down by the ruling clique, or filibustered, or shouted down. On a number of occasions Littledale was ruled out of order for 'reading a speech' which was contrary to Standing Orders. He was in his late seventies and had difficulty remembering figures, so this was an excellent if totally dishonest way of preventing comparisons being made between estimated cost, authorized expenditure and actual expenditure.

It might appear at first sight that this was the nature of such a document, which was a carefully produced broad brush approach specifically intended to provide a clear overall picture without bogging the reader down, be he member or not, in a lot of trivial detail. If that were to be a valid defence of the documents produced over the years, then clearly we might expect to find them free of trivia. We find nothing of the kind: a document in which the bottom line runs into six digits, or sometimes seven, has entries for items costing single digit sums, including repairs to the hydrants on south side, Stanley Dock in the sum of £0 19s 6d.[5] Evasions abound, the expression 'certain alterations having been found desirable/advisable/ necessary' being a particular favourite. Its real meaning is that 'this piece of work failed to function when completed as designed and it has been necessary to spend further money to correct the errors'. In short, there is at least some evidence for suggesting that in the latter part of the century, the Engineer's Report was produced not to clarify but to obfuscate the realities of what was happening, a tactic not peculiar to the Dock Board. Some engineers, however, chose, or were forced, to analyze their failures in order to prevent a recurrence, rather than adopt a posture of omniscience.

If that were so, then it would certainly be true to say that some of the members did not notice, or if they did, they did not care. One issue which made this clear was that of vessels anchoring in the paths of the ferry boats. The problem was discussed by the Board and by more than one committee on an intermittent basis over some twenty years. In the welter of discussion, which was at times quite acrimonious, it became clear that there were some members who had not the slightest idea of the powers or responsibilities of the Board, contending, for example, that they did not have the power to prevent ships causing danger to the public by anchoring in obstructive positions.[6] They simply had not bothered to read the terms of the Act of Parliament which established the Board, and neither had they asked the solicitor to give them a clear, simple and accurate statement of what it said. They were quite content to discuss the question on the basis of guesswork. It is a suitable comment on their attitude that when a ferry finally did collide with an anchored obstruction in fog, with the loss of twenty-five passengers, the vessel with which it had collided was the Brocklebank liner *Bowfell*. One of the members who had done his best to avoid any action to prevent such accidents was Brocklebank himself.[7]

At the very time that engineering problems at the north end of the estate were causing mounting debt and declining efficiency, the members found ways of filling the agendas for their meetings with items of breathtaking triviality. At the meeting of the Works Committee of 27 May 1892 a letter was read from the Variety Automatic Supply Stores Company Ltd, requesting permission to place their Automatic Sweetmeat Machines on the stations of the Overhead Railway. This was, of course, an error on the part of the vending machine company who had failed to realize that the Overhead Railway was being constructed by a separate company. The committee considered the matter and agreed a memo to the effect that the letter be sent to the Overhead Railway Company.[8] If the officers of the Board, several of whom were paid salaries of four digits, were not capable of making a decision as to what should be done with a misdirected letter, then they were not representing very good value for their salaries. On the reasonable assumption that they were capable of making such a decision, then one must query how such an issue got referred to a Board committee – and why.

The temptation is to assume that such issues were referred upwards in order to glue up meetings of the members with trivia so that the officers could get on with their jobs in peace and quiet. In at least one case this was not true: a long-running favourite time-waster was the location of huts and cocoa vans on the Dock Estate. Throughout the 1870s and '80s there are repeated agenda items dealing with these small structures, which were usually not more than about 8 ft by 6 ft and commonly mounted on iron wheels. They formed a humble but important part of the operation of the port, housing the men who dealt with the routine paperwork of the quaysides, providing shelter for supervisory staff and services to all the workers on the quaysides. It was obviously a matter of some importance that the quaysides were not allowed to be cluttered up with dozens of huts so placed as to obstruct the working berths or the passage of road or rail vehicles, but it is legitimate to question whether the detail of the location of such a hut was really a matter which need engage the attention of the gentlemen of the Docks and Quays Committee. In each case, however, a letter requesting permission for a hut was read to the committee, followed by a report thereon. The matter was discussed (usually only fairly briefly) and a decision made and minuted. That decision was technically only a recommendation to the Board, and then had to be confirmed by them, a procedure which normally only involved the reading of the committee minute and the granting of formal approval. Whether the permission was granted or not the item would still go back to the committee in the form of a letter from the applicant either thanking the Board for permission and agreeing to the rent and terms, or complaining bitterly at refusal. The latter could, of course, start the whole cycle round again. The request of William Mackay, Carter, for a hut at Victoria Dock was fairly typical, being considered by Docks and Quays on 10 March 1875, confirmed by the Board 11 March and response received by Docks and Quays on 17 March. The sums of money involved in transactions of this kind could amount to as much as £2 per annum, as in the case of Messrs Fletcher and Parr, who had three huts outside East Nelson Shed, upon which 'reports were read' (the number is unspecified) to Docks and Quays on 31 December 1873. In the case of a good cause such as the Liverpool Bible Society the committee might be willing to waive the charge.

It would seem that the reason for continuing to take these matters to such a high level was not the amount of money involved: it must therefore have been to keep careful control of obstruction to the quaysides. Yet on 2 June 1875, Docks and Quays solemnly went through the usual procedures before recommending that Messrs Richards, Mills & Co. be allowed to *remove* their hut from South Victoria, while on another occasion they required to know of the harbourmaster by whose authority he had allowed a hut to be moved by a matter of some yards.[9]

The harbourmaster was the principal officer responsible for the working of ships through the docks, for which he was paid the substantial salary of £1,000 p.a. at this time. He stood at the pinnacle of a career structure which rested on a multitude of gatemen, bridgekeepers, quay or piermasters, and dockmasters, and occasionally a harbourmaster had risen through those ranks to the important position he occupied: if he had not, he would almost invariably be an ex-master mariner. Unlike the majority of members, he was entirely familiar with the day-to-day practicalities of working every berth on the estate and he was in line management contact with those who did it. The decision as to whether or not a wooden hut could be moved a few yards was one which should have been taken by a dockmaster, on about 30 per cent of the harbourmaster's salary, perhaps being referred to him for confirmation in case of there being any 'comeback'. The suggestion that the harbourmaster himself was not to be trusted to make such a decision is preposterous, and the implicit statement that the gentlemen amateurs 'in committee assembled' were more competent is laughable. Yet it was not until a Special Committee was appointed to report as to the working of the traffic of the port that the issue of delegation was taken seriously. As late as April 1891, that committee had to recommend that, in future, certain matters relating to cocoa vans might be determined by the secretary without reference to members.

What this attention to trivia illustrates is that the members simply did not know what they were there for. Whether this was because they were compulsive meddlers is immaterial. The valuable resource which their time and energy formed was squandered by being misdirected. Their involvement in trivia prevented the application of their talents to the broad issues of policy which they should have been considering; their insistence on controlling activities which should have been determined several steps down the ladder undermined the authority of their senior staff and wasted their time in writing reports about the man, for example, who wanted permission to dive from the Perch Rock Light and collect money from the assembled crowds.

Early in 1882, the Bridgewater Navigation Co. preferred a claim against the Board in respect of damage allegedly done to their flat *Leander*. It was for £0 7s 10d, and the level of this triviality seems to have been recognized as excessive by the Works Committee, for they resolved to 'Recommend that the Secretary be authorized to deal with this and future similar claims, when the amount does not exceed five pounds, in such a manner as may seem to him to be most expedient.' This was endorsed by the Board on 16 March 1882.

Technically, the resolution applied only to the Works Committee, and was not overall Board policy, but it effectively became so when similar trifling claims were taken to other committees: similar resolutions were passed by the Warehouse Committee on 24 May, by Docks and Quays on 31 May and by Traffic on 12 June. The rapidity of the process is, of course, indicative of the frequency with which these trifling claims arose. At last, some measure of common sense ruled – for slightly less than a year. In late April the following year an employee of the Board made a small mistake which resulted in two bales of cotton falling into Waterloo Dock. The claim, which was for £4 4s 4d was considered by the Warehouse Committee on 2 May 1883.[10]

Problems of the Board and its committees being glued up with trivia were paralleled by those brought about for the Board's customers by the inflexible bureaucracy which was an almost inevitable consequence of the failure to trust members of staff. The *Porcupine*, a local journal of distinctly waspish style, published a series of seven articles in 1873 under the title 'How the Dock Board do Business' which consists of a string of complaints made by a highly knowledgeable commentator, probably a disgruntled officer of the Board. They relate to the lack of delegated power to staff, the inefficiency that followed and a nit-picking rapacity in their charges for warehousing and other services. The same year, there was published a small volume of abstracts of the proceedings of the Special Committee which the Board had appointed to gather evidence from its customers as to what improvements they would like to see in the port.[11] This apparent outbreak of 'customer care' was actually a trawl to find potential witnesses for the intended Bill, which eventually emerged as the 1873 Act, the same Act which was to blight and impoverish the Central Docks for the rest of the century.

The evidence given to the committee is perhaps best summed up by remarking that the Wine and Spirit Trade Association had no complaints – a state not only of bliss, but of solitude. Some of the complaints related to exactly the problems the Board was hoping to rectify, such as insufficient water depths, but others were less welcome. Several witnesses complained that while some berths were grossly overcrowded, others were under-used. Railway companies complained of lack of direct access to the quays, and the resolution of their problems would also have answered the cotton merchants' complaint that cotton was left lying on the quayside and then got other, later, cargo dumped on top of it. Goods were damaged by being dumped in pools of muddy water on open quays or in old open sheds, and there were insufficient hydraulic lifting appliances. It may be thought that some of these problems could have been solved without spending £4.1 million on new docks.

Ten years later, the Liverpool Cotton Association's Committee on Trade published a letter from its chairman to the Association President.[12] In this it is made clear that cotton merchants felt they were getting no better service than before: in particular it was implied that the Board had long known that lumpers discharged ships far faster than master porters removed the cargoes, resulting in congestion and damage on the quaysides. The same unwillingness to rock the boat which manifested itself in the various controversies in which Harold Littledale was involved was continuing to prevent any improvement in the service offered to manifestly unhappy customers.

For most of the customers, this situation had to be endured because there was no alternative. Even Birkenhead Docks, which were capacious, deep and under-used, were often disregarded as an alternative because of their poor communication with the mercantile centre of Liverpool and with the main cotton spinning areas. The Dock Board could, therefore, behave like the proverbial fat cat with cream on its whiskers – until 1885 when the Manchester Ship Canal Bill finally passed at its third attempt. Initial scepticism about the engineering and operational problems and an apparently widely-held belief that the capital would never be raised, allowed a year or two more to pass before a change of attitude became likely.

In 1888 the idea was mooted of the Board having a full-time salaried executive chairman. It is probably fortunate that this fell by the wayside, for it would only have provided the excuse for carrying on as before, by making available more Board-level time. It seems that there was a definite element of class distinction here: when discussing the proposed appointment of a general manager it was said 'The (dock) ratepayers are much better off with having an executive Board that they can approach and members of which they can meet on Exchange . . .' and again that steamship owners felt better able to trust 'a body of men who know what they are talking about from both sides'. The clear implication is that a hireling not 'known on 'Change' would have a communication problem.

But we have moved ahead of events, for those quotations are from the discussions on the report of a Special Committee which was presented to the Board at the end of 1890. The recommendations of the report itself are of less interest and importance than the discussions, for those reveal that there was at last a wish to assess the operation of the Board and to make improvements.[13] When Alfred Holt accepted the unopposed nomination as chairman on 15 August 1889 he referred to a future 'not entirely without anxiety, but I would put it no higher than anxiety'. A year later, that anxiety was growing and spreading and the terms of reference of the Special Committee were to investigate and advise on the conduct of the Board's business. When Mr Coke rose to introduce the report to the Board on 15 January 1891, it is clear that there had been a profound breath of fresh air; 'The Liverpool Cotton Association came before the committee with certain grievances which we were obliged to admit existed and which ought to be removed – grievances which had been before the Board ever since I have been on the Board and in regard to which nothing had been done.' Perhaps even more telling was his admission that in the committees on which he had served 'we have a deal of detail and exacting work to do and that by the time we have finished we are not willing to commence an enquiry and a discussion on some general question . . .' It might be argued that it was precisely those general questions which never got discussed which constituted the basic policy matters which should have been the normal business at member level.

Mr Coke continued to give an example of the kind of failing of interdepartmental liaison which was squandering money and goodwill alike. The Docks and Quays Committee, it appeared, wanted a shed and in response to their request, the engineer drew up a shed. This proposal, having occupied the Docks and Quays Committee and the engineer now went through the Works Committee and the Board, who both approved it. It was only at this stage that the Traffic Committee objected to the design, and the shed had to pass through the whole procedure again to get the plans changed. 'Our system should not have allowed such a thing to happen.'

The committee had made a number of detail comments on the unnecessarily complicated way in which day-to-day business was

Views from opposite ends of Princes Dock in the 1890s. This was the port 'at the top of the tree'?

(NMGM)

conducted, and the main proposal for improving efficiency in this respect was the establishment of a post of general manager. It met, however, with scant approval, and some of the objections were on much more logical grounds than those suggested above. Mr Rankin, in opposing the suggestion, urged that the existing principal officers should be perfectly able to deal with a much greater degree of delegated power than they presently wielded. His comment that 'You are trying to get rid of red tape, and trying to get the work of the Board done without red tape. Give those officers of the Board a fair trial . . .' went straight to the heart of the problem. Other objections came on less valid grounds, indeed exactly the sort of grounds which support the most unkind of the criticisms made of the Board over the previous years. Sir James Poole, for example, commented that Liverpool had nothing to learn from other ports and had a magnificent set of docks 'no wonder that we succeeded so well . . . Therefore as regards comparison between ourselves and other ports we stand at the top of the tree and have nothing to learn from them.' As a reaction to declining growth rate, declining market share and the prospect of imminent serious competition for the cotton traffic, this must be adjudged a mite complacent. Even Mr Coke, who appears generally to have been receptive to new ideas, had occasional attacks of complacency: 'we feel that at the present moment the dock estate stands higher than ever it did'. In his case, however, there was a strong admixture of realism, and his most apposite comment was that 'we have everything necessary to proper management if we apply our knowledge in the proper way. But we do not apply it.'

The central mystery is why so many knowledgeable men had failed to apply their knowledge for so long.

Neither the report nor the discussions on it are sufficiently detailed to provide examples of all the problems which it addressed, but there seems little doubt that Mr Barrow revealed the tip of an iceberg when he mentioned that friction 'sometimes arises' between the Traffic and the Docks and Quays Departments. Mr Parker went a little further: 'The cause of a great deal of our trouble arises where the functions of the Docks and Quays and the Traffic Committees overlap each other . . .' and it takes little reading between the lines to accept that his meaning was that a key role for a general manager would involve banging together the heads of the harbourmaster and the traffic manager. But he did not see a general manager as an answer, and expressed the fear that a man forceful enough to succeed in 'managing the outside business might also get to manage the Board.'

The second main recommendation of the Special Committee concerned the advisability of establishing a new standing committee of the Board, to be called the General Purposes Committee. Its purpose was to address those problems which, as Mr Coke explained, the existing standing committees never got round to dealing with, which included broad matters of policy and principle – those which are suggested above as being the proper object of the attentions of the members. It might seem, therefore, that the defeat of this proposal was another piece of complacent ostrich-headed thinking, but such was not really the case. It was precisely because the members were willing to admit that what had happened in the past was wrong that they were unwilling to allow committees to continue concerning themselves with trivia and to paper over the problem by establishing another one. As with the suggestion of having an executive chairman, the apparently innovative suggestion was really a means of maintaining the *status quo*, while the apparent inaction of not implementing it was in fact the indication of an intention to get things right in the future.

The Special Committee was mandated to continue its investigations in a narrower field, namely that of the everyday working of the traffic of the port: the Board had acknowledged that the root of its problems lay in the red tape of which Mr Rankin complained and in Mr Barrow's friction. The reader will readily recognize from many incidents recounted throughout this book that if these were not the full extent of the Board's problems, they were certainly among the most important of them. Even more important than that, however, was the recognition that Liverpool needed reform to stay ahead. Evidence given before the Royal Commission on Labour[14] suggests that if some of Liverpool's ways of going about things were bad, those in some other ports were indeed even worse. The description of grain discharge in the Port of London shows not inadequacy such as occurred at Waterloo but a complete failure to assimilate progress in cargo handling organization and methods. It was the nice warm glow which members had got from such information in the past which had allowed complacency to creep in: they now realized that if they were to continue to succeed they must re-adopt the old attitude of their predecessors the Dock Committee. To that body, the state of being ahead of the competition was a period of regrettable inactivity between strides to get further ahead.

We must not, however, allow ourselves to get swept away on a tide of optimism. The roots of the Board's problems were very deep, and all that the Special Committee's activities indicate is a willingness to try to dig them up. Actually to achieve that would take some time, as a classic Parkinsonian juxtaposition of 1893 will show. Years before, Harold Littledale had fumed over hundreds of thousands of pounds being wasted at the new North Works, and he had made specific attacks on the design and construction of the Canada entrance. On 14 March 1890, Alfred Holt, speaking as chairman, acknowledged that Littledale had been right, though not, naturally, in those words. 'The engineer's difficulty is to make a silk purse out of a sow's ear. No one might fairly be blamed for that.'[15] Such a statement is almost incredible to modern human ears: how was it that the designer and constructor of the sow's ear might not fairly be blamed for it?

But Holt's statement should have sounded strange to 1890 ears as well. Samuel Smiles, in a section laden with vitriolic irony, had castigated the terrible actions (or inactions) of a personified 'Nobody'. The passage occurs in *Thrift*, which ran through fifteen printings between 1875 and 1890 and includes the statement 'More mischief is done by Nobody than by all the world besides.' Given the popularity of Smiles' 'Gospel of Work' among the commercial classes, it is highly likely that this passage was familiar at least to some of the members. The idea was not original: it is embodied in the chapter headings of Dickens' *Little Dorrit* and even Dickens may have borrowed it from John Dent's 'Reflections on Nobody' published in the *Oddfellows Magazine* (Vol. NS VIII) in 1844–5. It is, of course, possible that Holt was being ironic, but if he was his irony does not appear to have had the desired effect.

If the engineer was not responsible, then the Works Committee must have been and the only excuse they could offer – being grossly and deceptively misinformed – passes the buck straight back to the engineer. Yet no word of censure, or even of mild criticism, of Lyster was minuted on this, or, so far as has yet been discovered any other occasion. Except one. In 1893, Lyster incurred the severe displeasure of both the Finance and the Works Committees, who told him in no uncertain terms what they thought of his prodigal expenditure. What, the reader may wonder, could he possibly have done which was worse

Fig. 7 G.F. Lyster, Dock Engineer, 1861–97

than the errors at Canada entrance? He had sent a clerk from his office to purchase some books of pre-paid tickets for the newly-opened Overhead Railway for the use of himself and other senior staff. They were first class tickets, and a book of first class tickets cost 2s 6d more than a book of second class tickets. He was ordered to have the offending tickets returned and exchanged for second class.

The machinery of this incident deserves explanation. On 19 May, Miles K. Burton, the secretary circulated what would nowadays be called a 'snotty memo' directing that 'First class tickets are not to be obtained in quantities at a time' and going on to explain that where they were necessary they were to be purchased singly and charged to petty cash. On 8 August, the Finance Committee read a copy account from the Overhead Railway Company for eight books of first class tickets for use in the Engineer's Department and it was minuted that 'The committee would be glad to know why . . . They also wish the first class tickets to be returned and exchanged for second class tickets. No books of first class tickets to be bought.' At their next meeting, on 15 August, they read a report from the engineer, and were unconvinced, for 'It was directed that first class tickets are not to be obtained for the use of any of the Board's officials' and the previous week's direction as to the return of the offending first class tickets was confirmed. This decision was passed as a memo to the Works Committee, who met on 18 August and read and approved it. The story comes to an end with Miles K. Burton sending round another memo stating that whereas first class tickets were previously allowable if bought singly on petty cash, they were now not to be obtained at all, by anybody. It is worth recalling that the difference in cost between eight books of first class tickets and eight books of second class tickets was exactly one pound and that Lyster's salary (following his reduction of 1891) was £3,500.[16]

If this extraordinary tale shows the secretary as a petty bureaucrat, such an impression is unfair, for all he was doing was complying with what Harold Littledale had so often called 'a vicious system'. In fact, his appointment as general manager in 1894 may be seen as something of a landmark in the transition to a more professional way of running the docks. It enabled the division of issues between the staff and the members to be reassessed along more logical lines, so that members interfered less and less in day-to-day matters and spent proportionately more time on policy matters. In the specific problems of access for large vessels to the docks they were supported by A.G. Lyster. There had been a major row in 1891 when G.F. Lyster had sought the Board's permission to reduce his own level of activity for the Board, and his salary accordingly, while passing to his son the work which he would no longer undertake. Alfred Holt resigned as chairman, partly because he thought this was a corrupt way of ensuring that A.G. Lyster would, in due course, automatically become engineer-in-chief.[17] In that, the events of 1897 proved him right. However, it is perfectly clear that A.G. Lyster's emergence from the shadow of his father also coincides with the beginning of the revival of the fortunes of the port. A frenzy of activity saw one long-standing problem after another resolved by 1914, when major construction work was mostly halted by the Great War. Sandon and Brunswick entrances were improved to take vessels of the size needing to use them while the irrelevant entrances of Toxteth and Harrington were closed. Above all, the need for docks which actually achieved the objectives of 1873 was recognized, and a new start made with the Gladstone System, the first phase of which, consisting of the river entrance and the Graving Dock, was opened in 1913. That scheme, which effectively outflanked the problems of the Canada Tidal Basin, was the salvation of the port.

At an altogether humbler level, that of the crumbling Central Docks, the new order was responsible for a rational approach. The infilling of Georges Dock and its tidal basin provided Liverpool with, at last, a worthy front door. It also enabled the Board to move from its various overcrowded (and in some cases insanitary) office accommodation into the magnificent edifice which stands there today. Happily, they were fast becoming worthy of it. A programme of passage improvements and shed building at last made a start on providing the coastal trade with the services it so badly needed. It was starved of funds by continuing large scale works elsewhere, but it was backed by an entirely new attitude. That attitude might almost be simplified to two figures: when G.F. Lyster built his Langton Graving Docks for the world's largest ships in the 1880s he laid its sill a mere 5 ft 6 in below Old Dock Sill. A.G. Lyster's new Graving Dock at Gladstone had its sill 25 ft below. It was designed by an engineer of foresight and authorized by a Board which no longer concerned itself with cocoa vans.

CHAPTER SEVEN

ODD MAN OUT: EAST WATERLOO DOCK

The Dock Committee was considering a further extension northwards before Princes Dock was finally completed and even before the departure of John Foster. On 8 January 1824, Timothy Grindrod contracted[1] for the masonry work of the river wall northwards from Princes Basin at the rate of seven shillings per cubic yard using free issue materials. While the work thus undertaken would not be wasted, the decision to undertake it at that stage represents an understandable failure to anticipate how rapidly the demand for berths for steam ships would grow, and Jesse Hartley rightly persuaded the committee that the priority should be changed to allow the completion of Clarence Dock before 'the new North Dock No. 1'. Work for the future Waterloo Dock probably did not stop altogether: in 1825, Princes Basin was deepened, and the considerable amount of potentially usable stone excavated was to be piled up for use in the new works rather than removed from the site. An agreement of 25 November 1826, for the supply of Runcorn stone to the north works provided for estimated requirements of 8,000 cu ft in 1826, rising to 22,000 cu ft in 1828. Unfortunately there is no indication of what proportion of this stone was for Clarence, but an agreement of 4 July 1827 makes it clear that some at least went to Waterloo: John Condliff and Ebenezer Rodgers contracted for the removal of a heap of spoil estimated at 60,000 cu yds from 'behind the river wall lately constructed' to the north of what was known as Billingsgate Basin – a small tidal basin used by local fishermen. Earlier the same year, agreement had already been reached for the building of the lock from Princes Basin to Waterloo. From about mid-1827 onwards, it appears that the scheme was left to tick over: it virtually disappears from the records until May 1831 (i.e. after Clarence Dock was safely opened and completed) when Hartley was instructed to proceed in constructing the southernmost of the new North Docks 'with all possible expedition'.

The expedition was necessitated by a continuation of the rapid growth in tonnage using the port. Princes Dock was already seriously overcrowded, especially in the spring, when large numbers of North Atlantic traders all wanted to make their first outward voyage of the year at the same time. Between the opening of Princes Dock and the instruction to Hartley, trade through the port had increased by a fraction under 90 per cent, but the acreage of docks in service had barely increased by a quarter.[2] Since this period saw rapid expansion of the importing of raw cotton from North America and the exporting of emigrants to North America, it seems reasonable to assume that the resultant overcrowding would be more acute at Princes than elsewhere. The new dock was specifically intended for these traffics.

In marked contrast to the extensive junketings which took place when Princes Dock was opened, the water was let into the new dock with little formality on 18 August 1834, almost three months elapsing before it emerged from the anonymity of 'new North Dock No. 1': the decision that it be named Waterloo was not taken until 7 October. It had been capable of accepting vessels from August onwards, but much still remained to be completed. Characteristically, no decision was made about the building of sheds before the opening, and Hartley's design – which was for his virtually standard open sheds – was not brought before the committee until November. Although the new dock was intended to accept the largest classes of sailing vessel using the port, it was relatively small at about 6¼ acres, and no pretence was ever made of its being anything very special: it was just another dock, shortly to be followed by new North Docks Nos. 2 and 3, Victoria and Trafalgar. The pressure to open Waterloo had resulted in these two docks which were part of the same programme, being held back, and it was not until February 1834 that Hartley was directed to start the major works of excavation on them.[3]

The early history of Waterloo Dock is, therefore, slightly obscure: involving no new technology, no engineering triumphs and no spectacular new traffics, it was just a very ordinary dock. It is perfectly likely that even if more information on it had survived, it would be of little interest, except in the question of identifying its

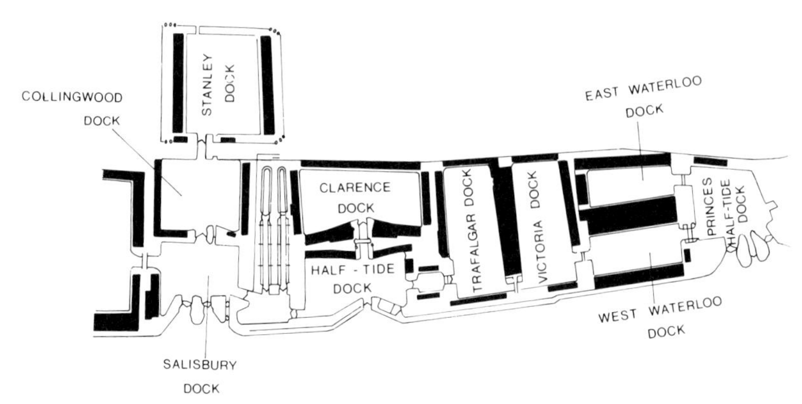

Fig. 8 *Central Docks 1870, showing the remodelling of Princes Dock Basin and Waterloo Dock. The small locks at Salisbury and Collingwood have been opened out*

trade more precisely. Unfortunately, even this is almost impossible: there were no specialized facilities, no appropriated berths and no scandals or disputes which would cause documents to survive. There is a good run of the dock registers, which in theory provide details of the ships which came and went, and of the cargoes which they carried, but the cargoes were almost without exception entered merely as 'general'. What we do know is that it was extremely successful, though perhaps the most telling proof of this is the simple figure given in the petition for the Bill which would enable improvements at Waterloo and Princes Basin. Kings Dock, which although old had been kept tolerably up-to-date, worked 7,100 tons per acre, while Waterloo managed no less than 30,000. (Both figures for the year ended 24 June 1854.)[4]

There was one facility at the old Waterloo Dock which was unique on the Mersey, namely the Liverpool Observatory. It is sometimes supposed that this was a research observatory, playing a part in the dramatic developments in the science of astronomy which were taking place in the middle of the last century, but in fact its purpose was far more mundane and practical than that. In the 1830s, when the need for an observatory was first suggested, Greenwich Mean Time was used only for the purposes of navigation, and for all other purposes local time was used. Liverpool's local time was about twelve minutes behind Greenwich, and the use of the word 'about' is quite deliberate, for the exact longitude of the Liverpool meridian had

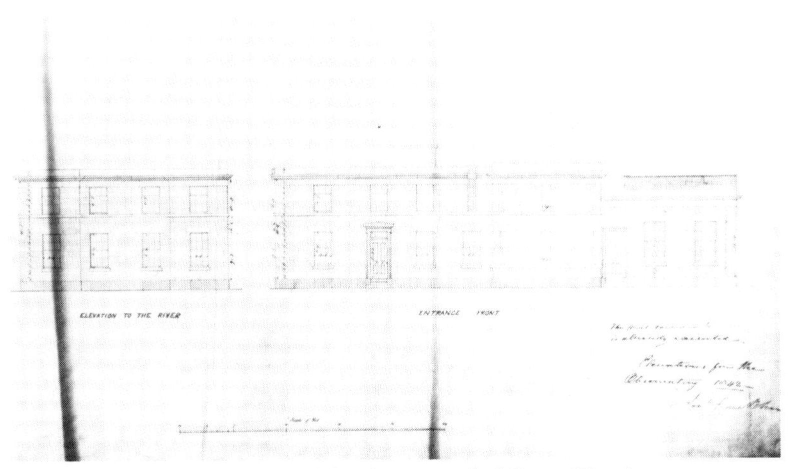

Elevation drawing of the observatory building at Waterloo (Colin Pitcher)

never been determined. For so long as the fastest means of communication was a letter aboard a stage coach, such differences were immaterial, but with the development of long-distance telegraph systems, first by semaphore relay and then by electricity, the discrepancies began to show and the fastest east-west trains of 1840 were already 'faster' travelling west to east than east to west. It was clear that accurate establishment of time at different longitudes was going to become a matter of importance.

In another respect, the calculation of accurate time from star transits was not merely useful, but a matter of life and death. The position of a ship at sea was determined by the use of its chronometer, and an inaccurate chronometer could perfectly easily lead to the loss of the vessel. There was a pressing need both for accurate time to set chronometers in the first place, and more particularly for a consistent preservation of accurate time to allow the rating of chronometers. Rating was the process of assessing the accuracy of an instrument at varying temperatures: if a chronometer lost two seconds per day at ambient temperature in the observatory, it was highly unlikely that it would still lose the same amount at tropical temperatures. The then state of the art of making timepieces precluded the possibility of having a chronometer which was completely accurate over a wide variety of temperatures, so the captain needed a table showing the corrections he needed to make according to the weather. A bad chronometer not subject to careful correction through its rating could easily cause an error of five miles in a day's sailing. Being five miles nearer than one thought to a rocky lee shore on a stormy night was a bad idea.

As early as 1834, Lt Jones RN had written to the Common Council on the subject of the keeping of correct time and the accurate laying down of the Liverpool meridian. In 1836 he wrote again, and his letter was considered by the Improvement Committee, but no action followed. In August the same year, William Lassell, a distinguished local astronomer, suggested that Liverpool needed an observatory and the following September, the British Association, probably prompted by Lassell, memorialized the Council on the subject of chronometer rating. In December 1838 the Liverpool Literary and Philosophical Society not only raised the issue again, but also pointed out the need for research into the magnetic effects of iron hulls on chronometers.[5]

The observatory was built by the Corporation on a site a little to the north of the present HMS *Eaglet*, and was a handsome and well-equipped building. Because of the odd hours astronomers had to work – observing at night and being available for chronometer rating and the like in the daytime, residential accommodation was provided for the astronomer and his assistant. These two were not, however, paid by the Corporation, but by the Dock Trustees, passing onto the payroll of the Board on its formation.[6]

There were two main instruments, a transit by Troughton and Simms and an equatorial for which they had provided the optics and smaller parts, but whose heavy mountings were by the famous firm of 'Maudesley and Field' (sic). There had been some concern that the impact of waves against the river wall might cause problems for the equatorial, but the work of Maudslay & Field, coupled with a massive stone base, provided a mounting which was praised for its steadiness. There was a sidereal clock and a meantime clock, and also a set of instruments for weather recording – barometer, anemometer, rain gauge, max./min. thermometers and wet and dry bulb thermometers.[7]

In addition to the precise business of chronometer rating, it was desirable to provide the means for ship's captains to be able to carry out a more rudimentary check on their timepieces, and the conventional arrangement was a time ball, a large wicker sphere hauled up a mast which fell exactly on the hour. By the time of astronomer John Hartnup's first Annual Report, the meridian had been accurately determined (at 12 minutes and 0.05 seconds West) and he was able to assert that the Liverpool and Greenwich time balls fell at the same instant.

There now arose an acrimonious controversy, in which Mr John Taylor criticized most harshly the decision to build an observatory in a low-lying position which suffered from salt-spray from the river, gross pollution from nearby alkali works and a truncation of its horizons by Everton Brow and Bidston Hill. The course of the dispute is wearisome, for it very soon resolved itself into a contest in which the original issue was obscured by a desire of the contestants each to expose the other as a knave or a fool. For our purposes it is sufficient to note that the Revd Mr Sheepshanks, another distinguished amateur astronomer in Cambridge and a man with friends in the highest astronomical circles, made a reasonable defence of the location at Waterloo Dock before rage and spleen got the better of him. In terms of the limited and practical objectives, it would appear that the observatory was quite adequate.[8]

Despite these limitations, Hartnup does seem to have managed to fit in a certain amount of more general astronomical observation. His main success, however, was in his prolonged and systematic work in chronometer rating, for which he used a gas-fired 'hot box' to expose chronometers to sustained variations in temperature. By this means he was able to establish (apparently for the first time) that temperature variation was by far the most important of the factors which caused the timekeeping of a chronometer to change, and that magnetic effects and disruption caused by the motion of the ship were relatively unimportant. Even quite good chronometers would vary by four or five seconds in the day according to temperature, and one horror story he told revealed an instrument which varied from 5.8 seconds loss to 14.5 seconds gain over a range of only about 30°F.

In 1855, the Magnetic Telegraph Company came to an arrangement with Hartnup to display a telegraph-controlled electromagnetic clock in the windows of their premises adjoining Exchange Flags. This was governed by an impulse generated from a master pendulum at the observatory, and was sufficiently accurate for chronometer makers to refer to it for testing their wares. Two years later, the

Town Hall clock, which was of traditional design and construction, was fitted with an electrically controlled remote regulator which kept its pendulum 'in sync' with the master pendulum at the observatory. According to Hartnup, this was 'The first large public clock to which this beautiful invention has been applied'.[9]

Eventually, the observatory shared the fate of successive forts, the shipbuilding yards and the fishermen, and was displaced by the remorseless expansion of the docks, disappearing to make way for the major improvement scheme shortly to be described. By the time this happened, and the observatory moved to the surviving building at the north end of Bidston Hill, the smoke and pollution problems on the waterfront had increased to such a degree that there would have been few regrets. Transmission of correct time by telegraph was such a routine matter by then that its location away from the docks was no longer a serious drawback and from Hartnup's important work on timekeeping, the new observatory was to move on to new challenges in the shape of tide calculations, but that is a generically different story and one which was not played out on the Dock Estate.

The Corn Laws have been the subject of one of the longest running and most voluminous of all the controversies addressed by economic historians. At their simplest, they were a series of enactments spread over more than two centuries of which the one which concerns Waterloo Dock was the last, passed in 1815. Their purpose was either to protect British agriculture from unfair overseas competition (including 'dumping') in order that the country could avoid importing food in time of war, or it was a conspiracy by rich idle landowners to grind the noses of the very poorest of the working classes. So much has been written to support these extreme caricatures and every imaginable shade of reasonable opinion in between that it is almost literally a question of choosing one's political bias and adding historical facts to taste. The campaign for abolition of the Corn Laws can also be portrayed as a chosen battlefield in the class war between the traditional landed rich predominantly located in the Midlands and the south, and the new manufacturing classes based mainly in Lancashire and Yorkshire. Certainly the fact that the main drive for abolition came from Manchester men with a great deal of support from Leeds upholds this view, and if we follow its logic for a moment we can see that it would have implications for Liverpool. If the price of bread is kept artificially high, then the additional cost bears most heavily on the poorest, since the proportion of the household budget spent on bread falls as income increases. That means that the minimum wage which will suffice to prevent starvation is substantially inflated, and what would be termed at the time an adequate living wage (which might allow such luxuries as a couple of ounces of tea per week) must rise with it. That increased manufacturers' costs. Figures collected by the Anti Corn Law League showed that single-income families, at wages from the adequate downwards, spent several times as much per week on bread as on accommodation, which was bad news for those who considered improvements in working class housing to be a matter of importance. Inflated grain prices even caught the industrialist in the rear, in the form of increased contributions to parish relief whether outdoor or in the workhouse. In the north, therefore, the Corn Laws were a burden to rich and poor alike, whose only benefit appeared to be to the rich and idle in another part of the country.

Liverpool was not, by the standards of Leeds & Manchester, particularly vocal in the campaign for the repeal of the Corn Laws, which is, perhaps, surprising in view of the participation of local men in a number of apparently kindred causes such as Catholic Emancipation or Municipal Reform. But theirs was a largely mercantile community, serving an economy which saw imported grain increase as a proportion of total consumption despite the Corn Laws. The repeal of the Corn Laws could only have one effect, though, namely a further increase in grain imports. The statistical sources offered in histories of the subject are varied and confusing, but what is clear is that wheat imports roughly doubled within a year or so of the repeal of the Corn Laws in 1846 and that, with large and numerous fluctuations, they continued to increase for the rest of the century. In one sense, what actually happened is of little concern here, for what mattered was the way in which a gambling man guessed what would happen: the Dock Committee was largely made up of gambling men, and here as in so many other cases, they backed the right horse. Although much of the grain which was imported in the first years after repeal came from mainland Europe, with some from North Africa and from Asiatic Russia, they made an accurate second guess that the real future lay on the prairies of North America, for whose produce Liverpool was the obvious port of entry.[10]

The new (1868) entrance to Princes half-tide, with Dock Offices and dockmaster's residence

(NMGM)

In the first half of last century, very few cargoes were carried in bulk. Those that were, such as coal or china clay, were delivered aboard by courtesy of gravity from staithes of one form or another and were discharged by vast and expensive labour with shovels. The decision to form a specialized grain terminal at Waterloo did not, therefore, imply the provision of equipment for bulk handling: that would be a second and decidedly innovative step. The Dock Board, inheriting the Dock Committee's sound idea of going for the grain trade in a serious way, took that second step, and asked Lyster to produce a scheme for remodelling Waterloo Dock to that end.

We may safely assume that the alteration in the general layout, whereby Waterloo Dock was divided roughly in half from north to south and Princes (tidal) Basin was greatly improved into a half-tide dock was the work of Lyster and his department. The triple entrance, with a small lock and two half-tide gates, was very much like that built

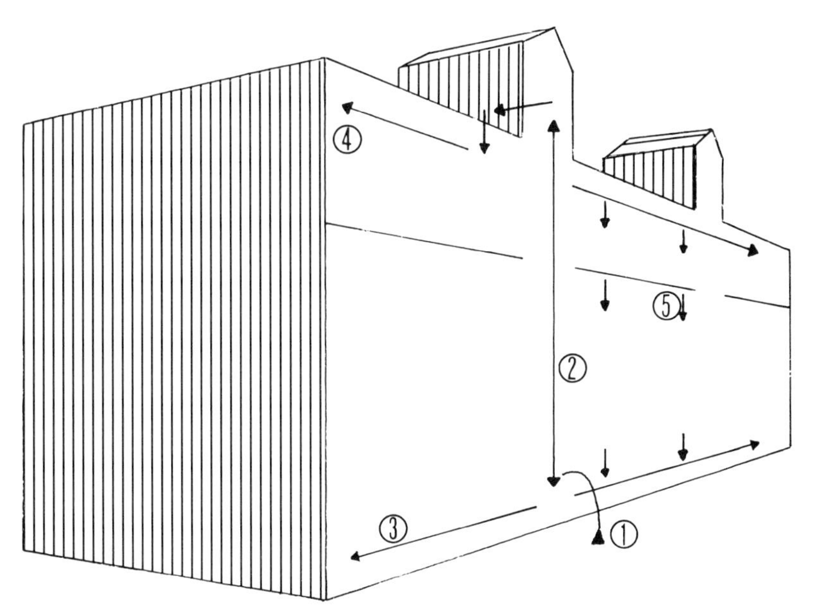

Fig. 9 Schematic diagram of Waterloo Corn Warehouses. 1. Tub crane 2. Elevator 3. Bottom bands 4. Top bands 5. Shoots (in every cell of every floor)

by Hartley at Salisbury and was undoubtedly an in-house design, down to and including the 'Hartley-Style' cyclopean granite walls. The idea of making East Waterloo Dock a cul-de-sac while retaining a through-way or 'spine route' through West Waterloo is quite obviously an antecedent of Lyster's later systematic and successful policy of the spine and branch. What was novel about East Waterloo, however, had little to do with any of Hartley's works and may not have had a great deal of direct connection with Lyster either. What came into being was a single purpose ensemble of dock, warehouse and handling equipment designed to serve as an interface between any of the various vehicles, road, rail or water, which might be used for the carriage of grain. The only system which approached this was the high level railway at Bramley-Moore, but as a component of an ensemble it was rudimentary in the extreme, being geared only to the transfer of outward-bound coal from rail to water. The facilities at Waterloo were not really intended to load bulk grain aboard vessels, but any other combination of road, rail and sea was readily achievable.

The corn warehouses were completed, nominally, in 1868 and were a truly remarkable achievement. They were the first warehouses for any bulk commodity in which all the transit requirements, whether inwards, outwards or internal, were met either from a central powerhouse or by gravity.[11] The only handwork needed was in assisting the filling of the crane tubs and trimming of corn when it refused to level itself in order to fall down a spout: everything else was mechanized. The building, often enthused over by those of a sensitive or artistic nature as being a fine piece of architecture, is nothing of the sort: it is one huge machine for moving corn around. The fact that it looks quite nice is an irrelevant bonus. What the Board was trying to avoid was the old system where cargoes of bagged grain were handled by a hoist or ship's gear, weighed on the quayside and then stored: by this method a rate of discharge of 300 tons per day was achievable, but only by employing gangs of seven men at the rate of up to fourteen gangs per ship. Even in the 1890s, where the old method survived it required not only large numbers of men, but also that many of them be corn porters rather than lumpers or dockers. The principle qualification for being a corn porter, and thus commanding pay of up to £3 15s 0d per week as compared with the dockers' 6d per hour, were size, physical strength and stamina far beyond those required in a docker. The corn porters' piece rates had regularly to be supplemented by 'hot money', 'dust money' and 'awkward money' indicating that some of the cargoes which arrived had been stowed in a less than expert manner – which meant, of course, that the rates of discharge were even lower, the costs higher.[12] As late as 1878 the practice still persisted in some places of measuring grain into sacks by bushel in the ship's hold before hoisting them and emptying them onto the quayside, their contents shortly to be rebagged, weighed and dispatched either to storage or use. The rebagging and weighing was undertaken by a gang of eleven men, but since grain was normally transported by the ton, it was at least a useful process. The bushelling was mainly useful for the calculation of import duty under the Corn Laws, which had been repealed thirty-two years previously. Leaving aside the enormous waste in the procedures described so far, one could continue with catalogues of increased cost every time grain was handled in sacks, finishing with the sacks themselves, which cost ½d in hire and another ½d in stitching each time they were used. It was estimated that, nationally, something of the order of 100,000 tons per annum of railway traffic consisted of empty grain sacks.[13]

The machinery for the corn warehouses was designed and supplied by Sir W.G. Armstrong & Co. and was based on the premise that it should be capable of handling about 250,000 tons per year, roughly two thirds in bulk, one third in bags or other containers. The reason for this apparent conservatism lay not in the means of loading or discharging, but in the fact that there were, as yet, no specialized vessels for bulk grain, and bulk could only be stowed in the lower holds. The fears for the stability of the ship which made this normal practice were enshrined in the Merchant Shipping Act ('The Plimsoll Act') of 1876 in the form of a prohibition on vessels carrying more than two thirds of their permitted loading as bulk grain. The result was that although the machinery was mainly intended as a new technological push in grain handling, quite substantial provision had also to be made for the old way of doing things. The Board had also, very wisely, hedged their bets by requiring that the warehouses should be capable of taking other goods, at least to a degree, in case some unforeseen political or economic change should leave them with a very large white elephant. The choice of contractor clearly indicates that an implicit decision had already been made that the motive power for the machinery should be provided by a steam hydraulic system.[14]

The pumping machinery which was installed was quite conventional, consisting of a two-cylinder horizontal pumping set similar to, but considerably larger than, those supplied to the Shropshire Union Railway and Canal Co. and preserved at the Boat Museum, Ellesmere Port. The weight-loaded accumulators, of the type which Armstrong had introduced in 1851, were situated at quite some distance (about 80 ft) from the engine, which was a far from ideal arrangement for control of engine speed or the suppression of water-hammer. Up to this point it would be pardonable to assume that Armstrong's increasing activities as an arms manufacturer were distracting attention from continued innovation in hydraulics. The boiler house was less conventional, containing five Field-type vertical boilers, which were very quick-steaming and were stated to deliver 300 hp while only occupying floor space equivalent to that of one Cornish boiler of 30 hp. The same source, however, gives the engine power as 370 hp which is clearly incompatible. Reversing the figures,

One of the preserved hydraulic pumping sets at the Boat Museum, Ellesmere Port. The engine at Waterloo was similar, though very much larger.
(Author)

i.e. boiler power 370 hp, engine power 300 hp, gives the result that four of the five boilers could just about provide sufficient steam for the engine, allowing washout or minor repairs to the fifth without loss of power, an altogether sounder arrangement which is what one must assume was installed. Even so, not much later in their history Armstrong's would have provided more boiler capacity than this in relation to the installed engine power and would also have installed two smaller engines rather than one decidedly large one, in order that any failure would only partially cripple the system. The engine was 'made duplicate in all parts, to admit of either side being worked separately in case of need', which would enable it to work with one big end bearing disconnected so that work could be carried out to the steam cylinder or pump on that side of the engine. The dynamic balance of operation at 60 rpm under these circumstances is a matter probably best left to the imagination. Little attention had been paid to thermal efficiency: the engine was a two cylinder simple, exhausting direct to atmosphere and apparently innocent even of an economizer, much less any of the more technical methods of saving steam which were by then available. This simplistic approach to thermodynamics was normal in colliery winding engines, where rugged reliability and unfussy driving characteristics were the most important design requirement, but in this case, almost forty years after the publication of Carnot's research, it must be regarded as a little primitive.

The whole dock had been planned as one hydraulically-driven entity, so that the movable bridges (three in number), ten ship capstans and twenty-four gate engines were all driven from the system. There was nothing particularly novel about these machines, except for the fact that nowhere else in the Central Docks was any attempt made to modernize passages in this way until some piecemeal work (mainly using second-hand equipment from more favoured areas of the estate) was undertaken in the 1890s.

The description of the hydraulic machinery has been, up to this point, fairly uncomplimentary. That which remains to be described was the clever part, the actual grain transit equipment. While there were some well-established installations in the United States of which both Lyster and Armstrong's were aware, the basic technology could not be considered well established, in the sense that a variety of means of moving bulk corn existed, none of them were yet very refined in detail. There was little or nothing in the way of systematic data collected to give any guidance on the respective merits of different methods. The extent to which nineteenth-century engineering concerns engaged in scientific research (as distinct from relying on native wit, inborn genius and empirical bodgery) has been the subject of historical controversy as voluminous and heated as that aroused by the Corn Laws. In this specific case, however, there is no room for controversy. In their efforts to develop and sell innovative items of weaponry, Armstrong's had for some years carried out scientific testing programmes in which products were subject to trial under controlled and repeatable conditions, dealing with one variable at a time. These principles were now applied to the problem of grain transit.

It seemed a clever idea to treat grain as if it were a liquid – in many ways it behaves like one – and to handle it accordingly. It was for this reason that extensive tests were carried out with Archimedean screw pumps, treating separately such variables as screw diameter, pitch, speed, and angle of ascent or descent. Screws with revolving housings were also tried, which had the advantage that part of the housing could be perforated to form a screen for the separation of unwanted particles, and the grain was well polished (making it more marketable) in the course of its progress. Unfortunately, the power requirement per foot run was considerably greater. In each case it was discovered that there was a definite optimum peripheral speed for the screw, above which centrifugal force started to throw the grain against the housing. Further increase of speed led to complete cessation of delivery as the grain was thrown clear of the screw.

Despite the fairly well-established use of Archimedean screws for transit of malted barley in breweries, it was next decided to consider the use of transit bands, or conveyor belts as they are now known. Concerns about their reliability, especially at the joints, proved in experiments to be largely unfounded, and the power requirement per unit weight per foot run was very much less than with the screw systems. The very long distances to be run (totalling over 1¼ miles) clearly favoured bands, and after further experiment it was found that an 18 in band was nearly twenty-five times as efficient as the tubular screw and almost exactly eighteen times as efficient as the traditional screw with static housing. In the light of savings such as these, the provision of an economizer in the boilerhouse was not a matter of great moment. The problem remained, however, that bands had, up to this time, been used for a simple transit 'from A to B', with no provision for alternative joining or leaving points for the commodity handled. The joining points were easy: all that was needed were spouts down which grain could not descend in greater quantity than the band could remove, but that was a very simple problem compared with finding the means of emptying grain off the bands. The device adopted was a triumph of ingenuity: running on wheels which rested on the underframe carrying the band, it could be moved to any desired position along the run. When not in use, it had two wooden rollers one behind the other above and below the band, and when it was desired to throw corn off the band, the winding of a handwheel brought the lower roller up above the normal path of the band, which was thus forced into a S shape between the two rollers and the grain was thrown over the upper one, falling into a spout which delivered it onto the next stage of its journey. To allow for the extra length of band needed to accommodate this operation, the whole run of band was made well overlength and tensioned by idler rollers with deadweight loading.

Even at this first fairly early stage of development in the storage and handling of bulk grain two problems were well known. Grain tended to develop a surface bloom, which was harmless, but made it look unappealing and tended to diminish its price even in the eyes of the experts. This could be removed by rubbing, and the cheapest and easiest way of achieving that was to send it on a tour of the building. The system of bands was therefore so arranged that it was quite a simple matter to empty one floor cell onto the bands and send its contents off for half a mile or so, every grain rubbing against its fellows and against the canvas of the belt and then return it whence it came. Should it still not look shiny enough it could easily be sent round the system again. The other, potentially more serious, problem was that bulk grain can begin to heat through germination and that heating is self-accelerating, leading in extreme cases not merely to damage to the grain but to serious risk of fire. The solution was once again to send it to cool its heels on a trip round the building.

It will be clear from several other passages in this book that the harbourmaster and his staff often had considerable difficulty in finding berths for all the ships wishing to use them. Under pressure, it was quite possible that he might find that he had a queue of ships waiting to discharge corn for the east block of the warehouses when the only berth he had free for a day or so was at the west block. The machinery was designed to cope with that situation, and should he then be so perverse as to berth a ship at the east quay whose cargo was for the west warehouse, it could cope with both operations at once. This flexibility appeared to offer a great deal of timely aid to our hard-pressed harbourmaster, and indeed if cargoes had been, as originally envisaged, made up almost entirely of bulk corn, it would have done so. Unfortunately the value of the provision was diminished by the fact that few ships arrived carrying only bulk grain, and the quaysides were not specially adapted for the effective transfer of bagged or other cargo from one side to the other.

The greater part of the rest of the machinery of the warehouses was made up of conventional hydraulic hoists and jiggers, for handling non-bulk goods. There were originally twelve hydraulic hoists, so arranged that their chains could be rove in a variety of ways to suit different purposes, and twenty single-acting jiggers on the outside of the building for lowering goods to railway wagons. These worked in pairs, so that as one lowered goods it raised the hook of its partner by an hydraulic balance. Ingenious and power-saving though they were, it was soon found advisable to make provision for a pressure supply to them so that they could hoist goods as well, and at a similarly early stage (i.e. completed by 1869) ordinary double-acting hydraulic jiggers were provided for raising and lowering bags, casks etc. at the centre of the buildings via trapdoors newly provided for the purpose.

We have followed the latter stages of the progress of grain around the building, but perhaps the most ingenious item of the whole installation was the grain elevator. Again there were various types of elevator in use in various places and working on various principles, but there was no established best method. Suction elevators, which would eventually become the normal technology, were at such an early stage in their development as to be both erratic in action and prodigal in power consumption, and ladder elevators were considered unreliable. The device which was adopted lacked the advantages of both those types in terms of constant rate delivery, but avoided their known shortcomings: It consisted of a hopper with a capacity of about 17 cwt, which discharged itself at the top of the building, and in descending prepared itself for the next filling. The intermittent action was not a serious problem, since the arrival of grain from the ship was not continuous either, being delivered by a bottom-door tub working from a sophisticated wall crane. In the original form, all this ingenuity was rather wasted by the parsimonious expedient of making the rams and chains of the crane serve for the elevator as well: while each was supposedly capable of handling 50 tons per hour, the business of changing over from one operation to the other meant that grain was not discharged at anything like the rate needed to gain the benefit of the excellent transit band system beyond. Separate cylinders and equipment were soon added to allow both machines to work simultaneously.

The warehouses themselves were perhaps the most impressive built on the Dock Estate since those at Albert Dock, and the only later building which is comparable in size and quality is the Stanley Dock Tobacco Warehouse. They are massive brick structures whose ground floor is an open colonnade to allow access for road or railway vehicles and to provide open space for 'leaving goods to one side' for short periods of time i.e. fulfilling the role of the traditional open transit shed. The piers are of rusticated stone with brick vaulting, and the brickwork throughout is of the very high standard of detailing and execution found in buildings designed during G.F. Lyster's term of office. There are five working floors, with a basement housing the band system and a machinery mezzanine above the top storage floor. The upperworks of the cranes and the headgears of the elevators and goods lifts extend for a further two floors and the towers which house them were clearly designed and positioned with a view to architectural proportion as well as utility.

The structure of the buildings was completed in 1867, and the installation of machinery continued through much of 1868, with monthly progress payments of around £4,500 made to Armstrong's. On 26 December we find the first entry for wages for attending the engines, and since there is also the first entry for wages for ash disposal we may assume that this was indeed the week when the system was first put in commission. Work was by no means complete – small amounts continued to be paid for 'fitting up and painting the engine house' until June 1869. A fairly constant entry of around £110 per month is headed 'supplies for engine', and may be assumed to represent its considerable appetite for coal. Coal contract estimates for the 1890s show the corn warehouse as consuming over 2,000 tons per year.[15]

If that were the whole story, the Waterloo Corn Warehouses could be judged to be a bold venture at the sharp end of grain transit technology, astutely undertaken at the right time to claim a large share of a rapidly growing market. Any failure in their profitability could be put down to the fact that the shippers were not as adventurous as the Board. Unfortunately it is not the whole story. The first indication that all was not as it should be was the usual overspending on the project. The works had been enabled under the 1863 Dock Act, in which the estimated cost was given as £291,671. Twice within that year, supplementary estimates were authorized by the Board, one for £36,596 on 26 January and the second for £71,773 on 27 August. Work on the site had only begun in July, with the construction of a dam across the Waterloo Dock, and the work of altering the dock itself then began. Princes Basin was able to remain in traffic until May 1864. Expenditure then mounted with fearsome speed: by June 1864 it was £41,954 and by 1868, when the dock was re-opened to traffic and the works appeared to be nearly finished it had reached £497,988. There were still some items to be finished and various alterations and additions were found necessary, raising the final total in 1871 to £559,353, or not far short of double the original estimate.[16]

Behind the overspending there obviously lay other problems which caused it. The first part of the works seems to have proceeded quite smoothly, because all that was involved was the well-known routine of building temporary dams to isolate the working area, digging big holes behind them and then building walls round the holes. The only thing which seems to have gone wrong at this stage was that it overlapped with the very large works at Herculaneum, and Kirkmabreck was unable to keep up with the demands for stone. That is the reason why much of the Runcorn stone from the former Princes Basin was re-used in the new works, and further supplies had to be obtained from Runcorn. The sills of the new entrance were being lowered by two feet (to 8 ft below Old Dock Sill) and the excavation

Detail of the basin walls, showing the enforced use of red sandstone brought about by the shortage of granite

(NMGM)

Interior and exterior views of the East Princes half-tide shed. The roof trusses date from c. 1840, reused from another shed

(Colin Pitcher)

of the basin floor which accompanied this produced a small amount of usable red sandstone. By mid-1866 the foundations of the warehouses were complete and the contracts for the ironwork of their structures had been let. During the next year the dock walls and masonry work were virtually completed, and the new hydraulic entrance and passage gates, capstans and movable bridges were in place. The east block of warehouses was nearly complete in its structure, and the floors were being laid, but 'very serious delay and additional cost have been incurred on this work through the failure of the contractors (as already reported) to supply the ironwork within the anticipated time. The non-delivery of the requisite stone within the required time has also been a further source of delay, loss and inconvenience.' While we know that the organization of the Engineer's Department under Lyster often left much to be desired, it is clear that here he was suffering from a problem which had infuriated Jesse Hartley at Stanley Dock and which afflicted just about every engineer of large-scale works at one time or another.

It had been intended that the whole system should be up and running in 1868, which is the date conventionally ascribed to the completed works. The entrances, water space and quays were opened for general use on 4 July that year and on 10 August the Liverpool Grain Warehousing Company moved into partial occupation of the buildings on the basis of an interim agreement as to rent for the parts of it which were usable. This was where the problems began to arise. It was understandable that there would be minor faults discovered in the layout of the hydraulic machinery: it was, after all, the first installation of its kind, and the chances of the engineers designing something which would perform ideally when first put to the test of everyday work were not very great. The result was a flurry of minor alterations to the hydraulic system, most of the changes being, like those mentioned above, to improve the handling of non-bulk cargo.[17] A more serious problem was that the cement flooring which had been employed did not prove to be uniformly successful, and considerable areas of it had to be taken up and replaced, a large and messy operation when the building was already in partial use, and which was accompanied by careful testing of the parts which had not failed. The result of these two problems taken together was that a further £38,615 was spent on the building during the year following its theoretical completion, and even that did not complete the work, for another £21,684 was spent in the year ending June 1870. The final account included another £2,065 spent even the year after that. There were some minor defects which cropped up as well, such as the flooding of the basement band channels in February 1869, though the expenditure of £35 15s 11d seems not only to have cleared up the mess but also prevented any recurrence. Some settlement of the columns of the arcade occurred, causing some excitement, but only minor repairs were needed, and the flexibility of the structure of the building proved adequate to its continued use for another century, suggesting that there cannot have been too much wrong with it.

On 12 February 1869, Lyster confirmed that the building was complete and ready for handing over, and the Works Committee gave every appearance of believing this to be the case. The Grain Warehousing Company took a rather different view: in a letter to the committee read on 2 March 1869, they declined to accept the building, alleging that both the warehouses and the machinery were 'in a very incomplete state', and suggesting that they send a deputation to wait upon the Works Committee to discuss the matter. It is clear from a casual perusal of the list of drawings of machinery at Waterloo Corn Warehouse that a great deal of designing and redesigning was going on at this late stage, and that the calm and scientific development described by Westmacott was not completely successful. To what extent that was the fault of Lyster and Armstrong's and to what extent it merely reflects fickleness on the part of the Grain Storage Company is unclear, but from the nature of the defects listed as the result of the visit of the deputation there would appear to have been serious design defects. Apart from the flooring problems already mentioned, and the foolish bits of parsimony with single-acting jiggers, it became clear that the transit bands did not have enough rollers supporting them, there were wooden components subject to severe friction which needed casing in metal, and the operation of the weigh-hoppers was apparently unreliable. The bucket elevator was of insufficient capacity to cope with the delivery from the crane-tub and was increased from 17 cwt to 1 ton,[18] while the crane-tub elevator itself was causing considerable aggravation, requiring 'alteration in detail to improve the working'. Westmacott's confidence was not shared by the Works Committee who added to their minute 'But the Board do not guarantee that the machinery shall raise 50 tons per hour.' The committee also minuted the extraordinary statement that the 'chains of machinery were to be protected from dust and put into good order if defective'.[19] This plant, it should be reiterated, had been in partial use for less than six months.

The failures mentioned above are not extravagant negotiating points brought out by the Grain Warehousing Company in order to postpone the evil day when they had to start paying the full rent: they are the complaints which after, no doubt, a certain amount of horse-trading, the Works Committee accepted as being their responsibility. Taken together, they show that new machinery was not only unsatisfactory and unreliable – that might well be a foreseeable penalty of innovation – but badly designed and proportioned for the work it was said to be able to do. As early as 6 August 1869, the Grain Warehousing Company was asking for the installation of 'American Elevators' at both Birkenhead and Liverpool in lieu of the crane tubs, and on 20 August, the engineer was authorized to erect, as an experiment, a small elevator of the kind suggested by Mr Spence of the company. He was also instructed to produce drawings and estimates for a scheme of proposed elevators – which shows that the committee was already contemplating the possibility of writing off the Armstrong elevators before they had been fully commissioned.

There also appears to have been a communication failure over the minor practicalities of working the cargoes. Grain cargoes had frequently to be 'stiffened' with 'kentledge' (an obscure word for pig-iron) and no provision was made for space to leave heaps of kentledge lying around before or after use. Similarly, wherever there was grain traffic, there were flotillas of flats and barges carrying small transfer cargoes, normally of bagged grain. It was only in May 1869 that a small crane was provided for loading and discharge of such cargoes: prior to that the small craft had to occupy prime berth space under the main tub-cranes or employ a jury-rigged arrangement from the hoists of the warehouse, which were not designed to reach out over the water. In details like this, as in the need for various extra hoists, there is no clear evidence whether the fault lay with Lyster and his department for failing to ascertain exactly how grain cargoes would be worked or with the company for failing to provide him with an adequate brief. In a sense it does not matter: what matters is that the end result was a building which did not work as well as we have been told it did, or nearly as well as it should. The consequences were far-reaching for the Board, and for the Central Docks.

By October 1869, while disputes over transit appliances were still simmering away, a further dispute broke out, this time over floor loadings. This became a complex matter in terms of its arguments and legal ramifications, but the engineering issue was quite simple. Lyster had worked to a permitted floor loading of 1,920 lb/sq yd in the belief that that was the contract figure, while the company believed it should be 2,400. At Waterloo, Lyster rechecked his calculations and decided that his margin of safety was sufficient to allow the compromise of stating that the loading could be considered as 2,400 lb/sq yd on the condition that no individual square yard should carry more than that, i.e. that the distributed load must not be averaged out taking walkways, hoist traps etc. into account. At Birkenhead, where the structure was less robust, the Board reluctantly agreed to stiffen the floor beams at an estimated cost of £6,500. Since there appears to have been no attempt to recharge this sum to the company, or even to increase the rent by the amount of the interest on it (as with extra hydraulic equipment) we must assume that they recognized that the mistake was theirs. There were two sources of this extraordinary confusion: one was that the original agreement had not made it clear how much dead space might or might not be taken into account when averaging the distributed load. The second source shows an even greater degree of vagueness in that there was much discussion as to how much a quarter of wheat weighed (on 29 October 1869 the Works Committee agreed on a figure of 500 lb). The need for these discussions shows that the building had been struck by the old bugbear of different people working in different units of measurement. It may be mentioned in passing that on 4 November 1878 the Warehouse Committee agreed a new scale of charges for various operations at Waterloo, one of which was bushelling corn into sacks. The charge for this service, which provided an accurate measurement of the *volume* of the corn, was made by the *weight* at the rate of 6d per ton. Such failures in communication and the errors they caused in a building costing £217,916 might seem peculiarly stupid, were it not for the fact that architects and their clients continue to succeed in misunderstanding each other to this day.

Additional and/or corrective works continued into 1870, and later in the year came to be marked by increasing suspicion and even bitterness between the Board and the company. The amount of communication between the respective solicitors increased, and matters went rapidly downhill until in June the company suggested the cancellation of all agreements relating to the corn warehouses. The Works Committee discussed this suggestion on 30 June, and tried to avoid a final breach, but a letter of 14 July from the company's solicitor discouraged them. An eleventh hour meeting of deputations failed to produce even a hint of agreement, and cancellation was approved on 25 August 1871.

The Board had never, up to this time, undertaken the entire working of a dock and all its cargoes for itself, but now found itself in the position of having to do so. There really was no alternative: even had there been another prospective tenant, the likelihood of a signature on the dotted line for tenure of what looked like a very costly white elephant was minimal. The removal of the grain handling machinery in order to use the buildings as general warehousing was equally unthinkable, not only because it would make the Board an object of ridicule but also because there was enormous pressure for grain storage space. Even before the final breach had occurred, the harbourmaster had been asked to report on the feasibility of giving preferential berths at West Waterloo for the loading of vessels which had discharged grain in East Waterloo, in order to push more grain ships through. His report was generally favourable to the suggestion, but he pointed out that the east quay of West Waterloo was sometimes in use by vessels discharging grain in sacks (presumably with ship's tackle) when berths were not available in East Waterloo.[20] Similarly, on the Birkenhead side, quite large quantities of grain were stored in general warehouses and even on occasions in transit sheds.

A small flurry of development now occurred at West Waterloo, with various extensions to, and improvements of, the sheds. The west shed was widened by removing its west wall and extending the roof to meet the west boundary wall, and a new shed was built on the south west quay. The significant additions, though, were small connecting sheds built between the east shed and the west warehouse, to enable interchange of cargo between the two. At the same time, the Docks and Quays Committee was involved in far-reaching matters of policy. At some date in 1872 Messrs Ismay, Imrie had placed an unauthorized wooden hut by their appropriated berth, and on 3 September 1873 the harbourmaster reported that it had been removed on his orders. Ismay's were clearly determined to have him put in his place, for on 5 November they gained permission not merely for two wooden huts, but for a dustbin as well. Next August the harbourmaster had his way when Docks and Quays turned down an application for another hut, but on 7 October Ismay's got their third hut.

There was, briefly, some doubt as to the legality of the Board's proposed course of action in taking every aspect of the operation of the new grain facilities into its own hands, but the Mersey Docks and Harbour Board Consolidation Act of 1858 was found to grant the necessary powers, and the warehouse superintendent was made responsible for everything which happened from the ending of the harbourmaster's duties as a ship arrived, to their resumption when it sailed or transferred to another dock. Matters then went fairly quiet at committee level, as the men on site got on with the job, apparently tolerably successfully. At this stage the work was being carried out in the same way as for general cargo, with lumpers, porters and stevedores assisted by dock labourers, and the first suggestion that corn handling was sufficiently onerous to justify an extra payment is recorded in 1876, which was a busy year in the corn trade. As a result Morpeth (general) Warehouse was receiving quantities of corn, and the superintendent there sought authority to pay the labourers a premium rate of +15 per cent as was the practice at the corn warehouses.[21] Unfortunately it has not proved possible to establish exactly when that 'existing practice' began, but a further step in the recognition of the emergence of corn porters as a separate grade came on 15 July 1881 when the hold gang working *Ingleside* at Waterloo refused to continue without extra payment. They were granted an extra shilling a day, apparently with quite a good grace. In the light of the frequent refusal of committees to allow sufficient powers to their principal officers, it is interesting to note that this decision, which clearly would form a precedent for future pay and conditions of considerable numbers of men, was made on the responsibility of the warehouse manager and only reported to the Warehouse Committee in the form of memoranda after the event. His action was approved.

The developments at West Waterloo were clearly successful, but suffered from the disadvantage of not being rail connected, with the result that prodigious numbers of carts were using the fairly narrow roadway between the east shed of the West Dock and the west warehouse. If the carts were delayed or were otherwise incapable of removing cargo as fast as it was discharged, then goods began to encroach onto the roadway, resulting in the whole roadway and the adjoining quayside becoming completely blocked. There was an obvious temptation to the carter to endeavour both to enter and to leave via the North gate, as the South gate access was via the swing bridge across the East Dock passage, which might delay him by being swung off for passage of a vessel. The resulting confusion in the roadway might well be imagined, and on 25 October Docks and Quays decreed that traffic should become one-way, entering at the North and leaving from the South. They also asked for the provision of a constable to attempt to maintain some semblance of order and No. 651, Roady, was duly given the somewhat thankless task 'to assist the traffic manager in regulating the cartage and in maintaining the line of stowage on the east side of the West Dock.' One feels little envy for the lot of No. 651 as he spent ten hours a day, six days a week in this uncongenial duty.

Alterations to the plant and the working methods of the warehouses continued. In 1876, the Field boilers, which had seemed such a good idea in 1868, were condemned and removed, being replaced with conventional Lancashire boilers by the celebrated mill-engine builders, Messrs Hick, Hargreaves of Bolton.[22] In 1878, the Warehouse Committee, after debating a serious issue involving the sum of 2s 2d, determined a rate of charge for grain boated across from the Birkenhead Warehouses for local consumption in Liverpool, which established beyond any doubt that there was a transfer traffic which had not been taken into account when the warehouses were designed. Neither, one may add, had anyone appreciated that where there is grain there are sacks, lots of sacks, and in 1878 both the LNWR and the L&YR were refused permission to leave a goods van permanently 'parked' at Waterloo for the storage of empty sacks. Quite where the Warehouse Committee did expect them to put their sacks was not made clear.

The following year, the engineer's report succinctly mentions that 'The lines of railway through these warehouses have been taken up.' This was not a rather drastic reprisal against companies which had the impertinence to want to store sacks, but the confirmation of a new working practice within the building. The original trapdoor hoists, lowering bagged grain through the building, occupied far too much useful gangway space when in use and had the further disadvantage that the man in control of the hydraulic winch could not see down the void. He needed a spare man to watch the load down, and even then there must have been some unnecessary danger of misunderstanding. A far better solution, the warehouse equivalent of creating extra space by making the kitchen door open outwards, was to use external cathead hoists discharging to railway lines alongside the building. In short, a return to the technology of the Albert Dock Warehouses.

By 1883, it was becoming increasingly clear that Waterloo Corn Warehouses were a problem. At the Board meeting of 6 December that year, our whistleblowing friend, Harold Littledale, alleged that there had been 'a series of mistakes and blunders at these unfortunate warehouses . . . in the end you have to pay £2,510 for not doing the thing right at first'.[23] That which had not been done right at first was the work of improving the provisions for retarding the spread of fire. In 1874 Littledale discovered that, other things being equal, a warehouse by Jesse Hartley cost 3s 6d per cent to insure while a necessarily more modern one by Lyster cost 6s 0d per cent.[24] Since then he had, quite rightly, continued to ask awkward questions about fire protection. The work which was required related to subdivision of spaces, but what is perhaps more surprising than that need was that instructions had also to be issued to ensure that iron fire-doors were left closed at the end of the days work and that 'openings in the roof over quays be provided with iron shutters'. Obviously previous practice had been very lax indeed, and the Salvage Committee had expressed its disapproval on at least two occasions earlier in the year. The work had been undertaken when it could be avoided no longer and in September the insurers had complained about the incompleteness of the work said in the engineer's report to have been done.

Grain transit machinery is very poorly served by the engineering press and the Proceedings of the Institutions, but one of the few papers on the subject was presented to the Institution of Civil Engineers that same year.[25] From this, it is quite clear that the technology of Waterloo has been left well behind. The author speaks dismissively of the storage of grain in 'flats' and estimates that a change to the vertical silo system would result in a saving on labour costs of £10,000 per year. The reason costs were so high was that despite the original research which went into the system, and the alterations which had been made since, it was still necessary to employ 'numerous gangs of men with shovels both for loading and discharging the floors'. The warehouses are commended, without ironic intent, for their suitability for the storage of grain in sacks. This expression of the obsolescence of the system provides a clear explanation for the worries expressed by the Warehouse Committee in their meetings of 28 March and 13 April about the losses incurred at Waterloo.

Later in the year a third problem came to the attention of the committee. As long ago as 1872 there had been evidence that the larger steamers arriving with cargoes or part-cargoes of grain were obliged to discharge partially into lighters in the river in order to be able to get over the sills at Princes half-tide and East Waterloo passage. The effect of this was an approximate doubling of the cost of discharging grain and the deficiency which forced it upon shipowners was in a facility not yet four years old.[26] Such large vessels were comparatively uncommon in the grain trade at that date. It is in 1883, however, that we find that they have become sufficiently common that a regular means of dealing with them, as a matter of course, is needed. On 24 November, the Warehouse Committee authorized the superintendent to employ his men in lightening the cargoes of vessels in open docks in order that they should be able to enter East Waterloo. It may be added as a postscript that in 1890 the harbourmaster reported to the secretary on the means he employed to try and optimize the use of berths throughout the dock system. 'I always use my best efforts to persuade owners to take their vessels into the Central and Warehouse Docks . . . but as a rule they decline to do so.'[27]

Whatever improvements to fire-break provisions had been belatedly made, they proved inadequate. On 16 June 1889 'fire broke out among some cotton bales lying on the quay floor at the north end of the west block . . . smoke rose through the warehouses via the grain spouts (which were of greenheart) and they were replaced with iron ones with self-closing iron lids.'[28] But only, it would appear, the ones in the west block, for in 1892 the Liverpool Fire Salvage Association recommended that such lids be fitted. On 9 November 1892 the Warehouse Committee authorized the work, spurred on perhaps by the fire which had occurred in the north block on 2 October.[29]

By now the original Armstrong tub elevators were a technological curiosity, but repeated requests from the warehouse superintendent for the fitting of modern bucket style elevators were turned down, and grain was increasingly discharged by the use of hired portable or floating elevators. The references in the committee minutes are vague, but it appears that at least two companies, The Grain Elevator Co. Ltd and The Portable Grain Elevator Co. Ltd were working there with machinery supplied by Stott's of Haslingden. On the Birkenhead side, where the larger ships tended to go, the Board had some 'floating hoists' of its own for handling grain, for these were reboilered in 1894. The apparent apathy about discharging plant at Waterloo was not, however, comparable with the level of neglect current in the other Central Docks at this time. In 1894, for example, considerable improvements to the band tunnels enabled the bands both to be doubled and increased in width, and in the following year Stott's won the contract to supply and erect a new elevator in place of the old 'American Elevator' which seems to have been the small experimental one of 1869. The new machine had a capacity of 100 tons/hour – double that promised (but not achieved) by the Armstrong equipment – and appears to have operated successfully once a small teething problem which caused it to fall on a ship had been 'settled by the solicitor on the best terms he can'.[30]

In 1898 the engineer was instructed to report on the feasibility of deepening the entrance and the passage sufficiently to allow ships of 3,500–4,000 tons to enter at any state of the tide. Although this represented a considerable amount of excavation, it did little more than keep abreast of existing tonnage increase: the average register tonnage of ships in the Canadian trade, for example, had risen from 1,580 in 1872 to 3,030 in 1897[31] and the indications were that the rate of growth was rising rather than steadying. On 20 July, the Warehouse Committee received his report and quietly shelved it, despite the fact that the previous March they had accepted the ultimate degradation of East Waterloo in the shape of allowing coasters to use it. Shipowners obviously held the facilities in no greater esteem, as on 23 May 1900, Buchanan's enquired whether they would be entitled to a discount if they agreed to discharge their ships into the corn warehouses at Waterloo or Birkenhead. The warehouse manager declined.

So did the traffic. In 1896, the Board had given an undertaking that, following the commissioning of the new machinery mentioned above, they would achieve an average rate of discharge of not less than 600 tons per day. On 19 May 1900 the secretary of the Liverpool Corn Trade Association wrote complaining that the actual average rate of discharge was about 318 tons/day from sailing ships and 826 tons/day for steamers. At that rate a really large sailing ship (such as the *California*, which is known to have used Waterloo Dock) would take about twenty-four working days – nearly a month – to discharge. Despite the fact that the Special Committee of 1890[32] had been well aware of the loss of grain traffic to Hull, Goole and Grimsby, the secretary was directed to reply to the Corn Trade Association advising them to persevere with Waterloo on the grounds that it was better and cheaper. The grounds for this assertion are hard to find, though the second line of his argument, that they would not be allowed to go anywhere else, had an appealingly simple logic. In fairness to the Board it must be added that the engineer's report for 1901 recounts the fitting of a new elevator in No. 3 Tower, and No. 2 Tower was similarly treated the following year.

Such measures were really only scratching at the problem, and a more interesting departure occurred in 1904, when a substantial part of the east block was let to Thomas Rigby and Sons Ltd which they proceeded to convert into a flour mill. The machinery was all incorporated within the main structure of the building, with a substantial polygonal red brick chimney added outside the south end, and a small red-brick office block built alongside. This latter was a domestic-scale building which bore such a striking resemblance to some of those built for dock residences in G.F. Lyster's day that it seems likely that Rigby's had actually borrowed some drawings. Their establishment was completed and in operation before mid-1905.

The Special Committee of 1890 had been responsible for recommendations which made the Board's business generally rather more effective than it had been, and in 1912 a Special Committee of Enquiry was appointed to look into the 'General Expenditure and Methods of Carrying out the Work of the Board', presumably in the hope that it could repeat the trick. It proceeded with grinding patience through matters great and small, never hesitating to suggest economies even where they would only save a few pounds a year. One of their recommendations was to employ outside master stevedores (instead of Board employees) at Waterloo, a suggestion

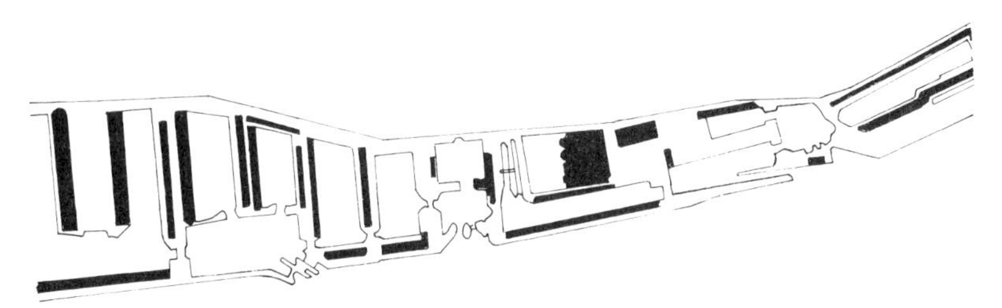

Fig. 10 *The Central Docks in 1949, showing the very belated solution to the problem*

East block of Waterloo Corn Warehouses during conversion to flats, July 1991
(Colin Pitcher)

As late as the mid-1980s it was possible to get the feel of the Central Docks and their 'hinterland' in busier times. This view of the corn warehouses was looking down Neptune Street in 1984

(Author)

which the Warehouse Committee could not fail to take as reflecting on the efficiency of their establishment. They therefore enquired, with a view to defending the *status quo*, as to the number of ships using Waterloo. Some time had passed, and the first quarter for which they got such figures was that for 2 September 1914 – 10 December 1914. During that time, six ships had discharged in East Waterloo, five of them at losses to the Board varying between £36 11s 0d and £350 5s 4d. The remaining vessel made a profit of £17 8s 8d.[33] It is difficult to imagine what action might have been taken upon this discovery had it not been for the fact that war had already broken out and it was entirely clear that every berth, good or bad or in the Central Docks, would be needed desperately.

East Waterloo was the only one of the Central Docks in which any significant investment was made between its original construction and the turn of the century, and the investment represented a bold attempt to capture significant traffic by adopting the latest and the best technology. Unfortunately, the technology was not only rapidly left behind by new developments but was not even successful in terms of its original specification, requiring considerable modification and still failing to achieve the tonnages originally promised. The boldness of the warehouse project was matched by a characteristic timidity in the matter of water depths, sills at only 8 ft below Old Dock Sill being obviously inadequate in 1868. It is perhaps more informative to think of the sills as being two feet below what was required by the comparatively tiny sailing ships of 1821 and imagining those alongside a typical steamer of the late 1860s. This error had become apparent within a few years of re-opening, placing Waterloo at a significant disadvantage in competition with Birkenhead. It should have resulted either in further major improvements or in a complete rethink as to what the dock and its warehouses were suitable for. Instead, with occasional lapses into activity, the Board allowed East Waterloo, like the rest of the Central Docks, to sink ever deeper into total inadequacy. The new river entrance of 1949 did not solve the problem, although it provided a new lease of life for Trafalgar and later Princes and Victoria. The north block of the warehouses had been damaged during the blitz and was finally demolished in 1951, the resulting open quay being surfaced to provide for its use by 'small coasters and barges' and the west block was demolished in 1969 to make way for the new terminal built for the Irish ferries and for Irish and coastal container services. At the time of writing, the east block is well on the way to being converted into flats, the attractions of its appearance having proved longer lasting than its adequacy for its original purpose.

CHAPTER EIGHT

A DAY IN THE LIFE OF A DOCK: AN EXERCISE IN 'FACTION'

The Mersey Docks and Harbour Board archives, extensive though they are, do not allow us to find out exactly what happened in a typical day's work in one specific dock. Much of what went on was so routine that, although recorded at the time, the ordinary working documents were not retained, and therefore many run-of-the-mill activities are known to us only from accounts which emerged when some dispute arose which was of sufficient importance to justify retention of the records. The account which follows is, therefore, a synthesis, but it is a synthesis based on a wide reading of the source material for the activities of the time in a group of docks whose history is, with the exception of East Waterloo, fairly homogeneous and where activities were largely interchangeable. The reader will recognize many allusions to events and practices mentioned in other parts of the book, but in some cases it has been necessary to draw on material from docks further afield in the estate. The timekeeper incident, for example, is derived from the Lynch case, which centred not on the central dockyard and its immediate surroundings, but on the Coburg Dockyard, and William Dock is, of course, fictitious.

All the activities mentioned were to be found in the docks between Victoria and Collingwood at the base date of 1890, and while there is no direct evidence that they ever all coincided in one dock on one day, the small firms of owners and managers involved in these traffics shifted around so often from one berth to another that there is no reason why they could not have done.

The outline of construction of the fictitious model dock is loosely

This evocative view of Clarence half-tide will serve to give an impression of the fictitious 'William Dock'

(NMGM)

based on that of Clarence Dock, while the account of what happened 'on the day' bears more resemblance to Collingwood than any of the others. Since George III, George IV and Victoria all have docks named after them, it seemed only fair to name the model after William IV, but the more serious purpose is to remind the reader that the chapter is not historical fact but an attempt to provide an impression of everyday life and work in an obsolescent dock.

It is important for the reader to remember that the public house machinations recounted relate to Board employees, not to casual dock labourers, who were not employed by the Board. Extra labourers, and tradesmen, however, were often engaged short term – for a week or two – by Board departments, most commonly by the Engineer's Department when more men were needed in widespread trades such as joinery, shipwrighting or millwrighting. There were, of course, official procedures for the employment of such people which did not involve sending a lad to look in those pubs where such practitioners were known to be found. The managerial failures which resulted from administrative accretion, as described in Chapters Two, Six and Nine, rendered these ineffective.

The resort to what is, effectively, fiction in a book of this type may be thought by some to be unwise. The reader may recall, however, the very brief account of the early years of Waterloo Dock because it was just very ordinary. Yet it was on the ordinary docks that the prosperity of the port depended, and it is to emphasize that often neglected fact that it has seemed justifiable to proceed.

William Dock was first proposed when John Foster was still surveyor, but the shortage of funds resulting from overspending at Princes Dock and the pressure to build a dock specifically for steamers ensured that no serious design work had started by the time that Jesse Hartley was appointed in March 1824. Parliamentary

Loading refuse in SHB Delta *at unknown berth, possibly NE Clarence, in 1926. By then, the barrows had been pensioned off*
(Liverpool City Engineer's Department)

Loading refuse into a boat at the Corporation Wharf at Chisenhale Street in 1935, to be boated down to meet one of the hopper barges. Apart from the Tilling Stevens petrol-electric dust carts, this scene could be from a day in 1890.
(Liverpool City Engineer's Department)

powers were obtained in 1827, for a basin of just over five acres with entrances on both north and south sides. The passages were, and still are, 45 feet wide and the depth is 6 feet below Old Dock Sill. Access from the river is now via Salisbury and Collingwood Docks, but originally the north passage opened into a small tidal basin which had been provided mainly for the use of local fishing craft as the northward progress of the river wall prevented them from beaching their boats as they had done in the past. William Dock was opened in 1833 amid some rejoicing in the cotton trade, which had been very active in lobbying for its construction.

By September 1890 it presents a fairly sad sight. Briefly the centre of the greatest oceanic trade the world had ever seen to date, it can now accommodate only coastal craft, and not even the biggest of those.[1] At the north-east quay rise continuous clouds of dust which have settled over a period of years on all the adjacent buildings, rendering them a streaky grey-brown colour, with just the occasional tinge of rust or the more occasional hint of green paint showing through. The source of all this is the Corporation rubbish berth. The good citizens of Liverpool produce, in round figures, one ton of ash per head per year, and much of it together with the rest of their general dustbin refuse, is loaded into steam hopper barges, taken out beyond the Bar and dumped. An occasional refuse cart or wagon makes its way in and out, its emptying being marked by an intensification of the dust-cloud. Watching the loading process it is hard to realize that this berth is in one of the great ports of the world and that barely half a mile away the Cunard's mighty *Umbria* is taking on

SHB Beta *loading overside in 1908, as described for 'William Dock'. It is actually NE Collingwood.*
(Liverpool City Engineer's Department)

cargo and stores in altogether more salubrious surroundings. Hopper barge *Beta* is already fairly well laden, so that as each of the eight men loading her walks along his barrow-run and tips another barrow-load, another small cloud arises. They use a special shape of barrow, very wide and shallow, to reduce the risk of awkward-shaped bits falling out. Wet weather relieves the loaders of the dust problem, but makes the work much harder as the refuse is both heavier and harder to shovel and tip. Their lot in life is not improved by the fact that the surface from which they shovel the refuse is still formed of beach cobbles laid the year after the dock opened.[2] But this is happily atypical: the greatest part of *Beta*'s cargo now arrives by boat from the Corporation Canal Wharves, in bottom emptying containers. This greatly reduces the hard labour, but does nothing to diminish the clouds of ash.

Behind the heap of refuse, a dock policeman is doing his inadequate best to maintain something like law and order among a band of about twenty irate and foul-mouthed carters who are trying to get to the west shed. The reason they cannot get there is that two days ago a heavy haulage firm delivered a marine boiler to the north-west berth, and strained the old double-leaf cast iron swing bridge at the passage. Jesse Hartley designed good bridges, but he did not design them with thirty-ton boilers drawn by traction engines in mind. Three men and a boy from the Engineer's Department are attempting to get the bridge to function properly again, with much moving of pig-iron ballast, driving of steel wedges and stopping to think about it. Periodically they have a desultory tug at the hand-operated bridge engine and decide that the bridge is, as it appears, still stuck, part open, part closed. Normally this would not be a problem, as the carters could turn round and go to the bridge over the South passage, but irritations never come singly, and the South passage is temporarily obstructed by the two very earnest-looking young men supervising the swinging of a lead from the bow of a tug which is firmly occupying the passage.

Two weeks ago, the Waterford steamer grounded in this passage, and was slightly damaged, resulting in a claim against the Board. The company contended that the three sister-ships of that class went in and out via that passage three times a week without trouble, and that the damage must be occasioned by the passage invert rising. The Works Committee were, of course, having none of that and pointed out that the skipper had been moving out stern first and too fast. When he realized his mistake he had briefly ordered full ahead to lose speed, and being still in the passage, pulled down his stern onto the sill. A Board diver has confirmed that the sill is damaged, for which the Board is making a counter-claim. The two earnest young men are, respectively, from the engineer's office and from the company's solicitors. The former is attempting to convince the latter that, so far from the invert being higher than it should be, it is lower as the result of the damage caused. While they will not agree on this point, and the dispute will continue for months, they are quite agreed that what they are doing is much more important than any consideration of moving out of the way to let the carters get on with their work.[3]

A purposeful figure strides from the west quay towards them. It is the skipper of the Western Isles Packet, which has finished loading flour, tinned food, bottled beer and barrels of lamp oil, and is ready to leave on the tide in a couple of hours. For this occasion he has put on a gold braided cap and laid aside his leisurely church-warden pipe for a carefully selected short, aggressive briar. The young men have some difficulty in understanding his accent, but the colour of his complexion, the gestures with the stem of the pipe and the use of certain expressions, which are recognizable by their inflexion in any language, eventually get the message across that he does not think that the Engineer's Department is doing its best for a regular paying customer when they obstruct both passages from the dock at the same time. On the far side of the passage, a small group of seamen and dock workers are obviously enjoying the contest, as the irate Scotsman continues to berate organizations where the right hand does not know where the left is going. Then a happy thought occurs to him, and he roars across the passage to them 'Is there a telegraph this side of the dock?' and is somewhat amazed when he is told, rather respectfully (for the dockers know he intends to start a real row), that there is a new telephone at the canteen on the north-west corner.

As he turns to walk to the canteen, he hears appalling grinding noises from the far end of the dock followed by an ironic cheer from the assembled carters. It transpires that the balance of the swing bridge had actually been quite reasonable several attempts ago, and that the real problem was the broken piece of ballast which had fallen onto the track, wedging one of the rollers. A thick coat of thought had suggested that brute force would probably succeed where ingenuity had failed, and an old wooden capstan, disused since sailing craft virtually ceased to use the dock, had been pressed into service along with much rope, many pulley blocks and a borrowed horse, to persuade the bridge to override the obstruction. But the Scotsman rarely has a chance to use a telephone, and still feels inclined to let the engineer's office have the benefit of his advice on the subject of work scheduling, so he continues on his way.

The canteen is a long, low building which looks a bit like a small transit shed of the new kind. It has been built with very little regard for style, but is well constructed of local brick, nicely laid in English Bond and with a bit of ornamental corbelling. The only real extravagance on the outside is a large terracotta plaque reading 'Dock Workers' Dining Room 1875'. When first opened, it was built and run by the Docks and Quays Committee as a welfare provision for the workers. A certain element of idealism was evident in the provision of a small library, but there was also an element of business realism in that it was intended to be sufficiently attractive to reduce the incentive for men to patronise any one of the nine pubs which stood within a fifty yards' lurch of the gate on the Dock Road. Inside, it is somewhat grubby, but cleaner than might be expected, given the proximity of the rubbish berth, and its double doors keep out much of the noise and dust. No heating system is apparent, nor is any necessary, as most of one end of the building is occupied by a huge cast iron range and an equally huge steam-bath for keeping food hot. The air is thick with smoke from the tobaccos of all nations.

After the novelty had worn off, the popularity of the 'Dining Room' waned sharply, for reasons which can, perhaps, be deduced just from that choice of title. To their credit, the Docks and Quays Committee recognized the problem, and suggested that the men who worked regularly in the area should elect a committee to be responsible for its management, and the canteen now serves a couple of hundred meals a day. The library is not much used, indeed its only occupants are usually those more thoughtful members of the worker community who read the business columns of the *Liverpool Courier*, which stands on a large wooden lectern there. From this they are able to find out what they would otherwise never know, namely what the Dock Board and its committees do. Today, they are studying last Thursday's issue very closely, for earlier this morning there were two very important looking men on the east quay, one of whom was thought to be the engineer-in-chief, so they are looking for the report of last week's Works Committee Meeting to see whether the long-rumoured modernization of William Dock is mentioned. That would account for the visitation.[4]

The swing bridge has been back in action for a little while now, and one of the unfortunates released is a portly gentleman in city clothes who enters the canteen and confidently enquires of the assembled company whether any of them is from the *Anna Marie*, at which a small man emerges reluctantly from behind a very large mug of tea and admits to being bosun of the vessel. She is lying at the north-west quay, having arrived last Monday with over half her cargo made up of bulk grain. She was berthed in East Waterloo, where she was allowed to discharge the general merchandise stowed above the grain, but when the grain was reached it was found to be more than a little weevilly, so *Anna Marie* and her unwanted guests were rapidly removed from Waterloo to await the attention of an arbitrator who would assess the amount of the loss and its probable cause. That is the mission of the smartly attired gent who has arrived, and he seems a little displeased when he realizes that *Anna Marie* is lying outside of *Pigeon*, which has just finished discharging its cargo of untreated hides and is now waiting for a graving dock for her annual survey. While the hides themselves are now making their smelly way up the canal to Litherland Tannery, *Pigeon* is still slimy all over and capable, as the gentleman would no doubt put it, of causing considerable offence to the olfactory organ. The deck-hand on *Pigeon*, who is seated against the winch making a small rope fender for the ship's lifeboat, watches furtively, hoping for the amusement of seeing the city gent land backside first in the slime, but is disappointed. What he could not know, of course, is that thirty years ago this corn merchant was a master in sail, bringing grain from Chile to Liverpool, and advancing years and waistline have not robbed him of his ability to keep his footing.

The bosun of *Anna Marie* already has one of the hatch-covers rigged to the forecastle winch, but the boiler-pressure is well down and the steam is very wet so there is a fair amount of puffing and spraying of water before the winch agrees to do its work. As the hatch-cover begins to lift, the arbitrator gets as close as he dares to have a smell of the cargo before too much fresh air gets to it, and the expression on his face suggests that he is not impressed with its quality. Before he climbs down into the hold, he produces some small glass sample jars from his bag, which he stuffs into his pockets. Some minutes later he emerges with full sample jars, which he compares with the sample from his bag which was that on the basis of which the cargo had been purchased. The bosun hovers slightly anxiously, in case some misdeed of his when loading might have introduced the weevil, but he need not worry. 'You say your passage was fourteen days? then you are clear, for there is so much weevil in this sample that it must have been present and breeding rapidly when this sales sample – which is plainly fraudulent – was supposedly taken. I shall put my name to that. My view is that the grain is so bad that it should be dumped at sea, but you had best wait your company's authority.'[5]

This was not a good day for the arbitrator's nose, for as he left for his office, a small Irish steamer which had arrived first in on the tide began to discharge cattle on the berth to the west of the rubbish boat. Cattle which have been at sea for a day or two are not a pleasing sight, and have an even less pleasing smell, a smell of which he got the full benefit as he had to pass some of them on the bridge on the first stage of their last walk to the abattoir just up the road.

The Scottish skipper is on his bridge, cap off again, whisky in hand, talking to his engineer who is, in turn, passing instructions down the speaking tube to his only assistant. The engine is idling gently forward and a few wisps of steam drift from the engine room skylight: there has been a problem with water in the LP cylinder, but it has cleared itself out and warmed through, and they are ready to sail when they hear the bell from the clock tower.

The vessel ahead is also showing signs of readiness to sail. She is bound for Dublin with a cargo mainly of cotton goods, but ahead of her there is still feverish activity as the crew of *Astrid* try to finish loading the casks of nails, nuts, bolts and screws which had been kept waiting on the wrong side of the disabled bridge. Theirs is a tramp ship, bound for Drogheda, and missing this tide will effectively destroy virtually all the profit on the voyage. The stevedores and their labourers are doing their best to help, and there are no less than fourteen of them rolling casks, applying grab slings which grip the casks by the end of the staves, and working the crane. The crane is a worthy piece of equipment. Jesse Hartley had been authorized to erect it in 1845, when he made a number of minor alterations to the original open shed which he had built there twelve years before. He installed a three-ton hand crane, with a pivoting wooden jib in line with the columns, and made a strange-shaped cut-away in the overhang of the roof to allow it to slew round through very nearly 180°.[6] It was a good piece of equipment in 1845, when hydraulic hoists had not been invented, and neither had steam deck winches, but in 1890, used in a hurry, it seems nearer to the technology which built the pyramids than that which is loading *Umbria*. Valiant though their efforts are, the effect is trifling compared with the performance of the ship's own derrick and winch.

In the opposite corner of the dock, two sailing flats have arrived from Widnes with cargoes of chemicals bound for Portugal. The only regular foreign trader in William Dock is the Hughes 'line'. Actually, the Hughes Line does not own any ships, and if it did it would probably have better judgement than to buy any of the ones it manages. They were the leading edge of technology forty years ago, but now they are rust buckets. Each is owned by a single-ship company, so that in the quite likely event of disaster that company, whose assets consist of one rusty ship and three weeks' unexpired rent on a wooden hut on the quayside, can be liquidated. Such vessels tend to attract crews of less than sterling worth, and the captain of the *Calliope* whose presence is eagerly awaited at the Hughes Line appropriated berth, was dismissed by Harrison's and subsequently imprisoned for committing an unnatural offence against a boy cook. His mate is said, by some, to have been sober on Ash Wednesday 1885. The skippers of the flats have taken good care to tie up in a position where they hope *Calliope* cannot possibly collide with them, knowing only too well that many a flat master has been drowned in dock that way.

Back on the west side, *Astrid* has completed loading and her crews are battening down the hatch-covers. Some sort of transaction involving bottles of whisky appears to be going on between the mate and two stevedores and it may be that these have some bearing on the speed with which she has got ready for sea. A small man in a small wooden hut, who has been recording the cargo as it was loaded has apparently been helpful as well. 'Caught in the act!' a voice booms behind them as they conceal their corrupt gains about their persons. But they do not spin round in expectation of the instant dismissal that awaits those caught accepting such inducements,[7] for they recognize the voice. It is not the assistant traffic manager, it is Holy Joe. For years, Holy Joe has plied the quays of William and the adjoining docks often at considerable danger to himself and usually to the annoyance of those he meets. His fire and brimstone evangelism is not endearing, and he would never have survived the resolute attempts of two different piermasters to have him barred from the docks were it not for the fact that the Chairman of the Mission from which he comes is also a member of the Board. Even so, it is an undoubted Holy Miracle that he has never been thrown in the dock, so astute is he at saying exactly the wrong thing at the wrong time. But the stevedores are rescued by the arrival of a messenger boy enquiring for the whereabouts of the flat *Polly*, for Joe, seeing a young impressionable potential convert, undoubtedly a better prospect than they are, kindly takes the lad off to the skipper of *Polly*, who is in a bosun's chair hung from a timberhead painting a fancy scroll on his rudderstock while awaiting the *Calliope*. 'Telegraph message, Sir. *Calliope* boiler exploded off Great Ormes Head. Await further orders.' The skipper is foolish enough to remark that this awaiting could gainfully be done in the comfort of nearby licensed premises, which provokes a diatribe of no relevance to this narrative, during which the messenger boy escapes.

While these mildly unplanned or unpleasant activities proceed at the other quays, the east quay is a model of quiet efficiency. It is the one part of the dock which has been modernized. Instead of the weatherboarded open sheds on the other sides, it has a single, neat brick built shed with continuous sliding doors along the full length of its waterside. At the far side, and in each end, it has sliding doors twelve feet square, and its floor is actually a deck built to the height of the floor of a railway wagon. Along its back wall runs a railway siding, on which stands a small train of wagons stacked with crates. Its floor is of smooth asphalt, so that the porter's trucks which the labourers are using to transfer the crates run easily and without the load falling sideways. They are working two hatches of the ship alongside, a Belfast boat which is built more or less to the last inch that can be got into the old docks in this part of the port. The ship's tackle is in use on one hold, and two hydraulic jiggers are working the other with silent effortlessness. Not all the goods on the train are for this ship: a small stack of crates of machinery spare parts bound for Buenos Aires is standing by the end door of the shed awaiting a cart to arrive to transfer them to Kings Dock. The ship's second derrick is working over the other side, with a large tub, raising coal from one of two Leeds and Liverpool boats which have come down from Wigan, and are tied up alongside. This is how the Board would like to imagine their docks working, or nearly so. There does seem to have been some slight delay in the removal of 100 tons of potatoes which arrived from Dublin yesterday and which are occasionally getting under people's feet. No one seems quite sure when the railway wagons for them will arrive.[8]

Even odder, however, is what is happening in the corner of the shed. A Customs officer is talking to a Roman Catholic Priest and both are looking in some mystification at an enormous statue of the Virgin Mary. Of course, all the Customs man wants to know is its value, but the reason he does not know it is that it was discharged there from a Hughes liner. It had been despatched to 'Father Murphy, Liverpool' from Brazil, where it was made, via Lisbon which was where the Hughes Line came into the picture. As may be imagined, there is more than one Father Murphy in Liverpool, but not one of them is expecting an enormous statue from Brazil. The Hughes Line's paperwork, up to the standard of their boiler inspecting, has revealed nothing, and the present priest, whose name is not Murphy, is the incumbent of the new church of St Alban nearing completion about a quarter of a mile away. The traffic manager, concerned at making his books balance, asked his committee what he should do about the mounting penalty rent due on a statue which had outstayed its 48-hour welcome, and suggested that possibly the priest might buy it for his new church. The Board, being more generous, have offered to give it to the church, writing off the rent with the gift, but are concerned that they do not end up liable for any duty on it. The Customs man does not appear to have anything in his book which covers the situation, and eventually decides that there is more paperwork threatened here than the whole business is worth. The statue is written off his books too, sheeted up and arrangements made with a carter, whose name really is Murphy, for it to be delivered to the church at a price which will do more good to his soul than his wallet.[9]

One thing which always annoys the men who work with cargoes and the ships and vehicles that carry them is the common assumption that they are unskilled, and that all the job needs is physical strength coupled with an unusual tolerance of bad working conditions. When, therefore, they see someone doing it wrong, they derive enormous amusement as well as satisfaction from the ego-boost delivered. A couple of sharp-eyed gatemen have already spotted a potential comic interlude arriving as they stand oiling their gate engines and waiting for the order to close the gates. Just by the old north-west shed is a small low-sided wagon bearing the name of the Shropshire Union Railway and Canal Company. Its load stands about five feet above the tops of the wagon sides and is swaying lumpily and irregularly within the tightly-drawn tarpaulin that covers it. The gatemen know what is inside, and gradually a small audience of assorted dock workers begins to gather: they have identified a load of lavatory pans.[10]

Lavatory pans are among the most difficult of all loads to stow, which is why the Staffordshire manufacturers dispatch them by canal whenever possible. They are bulky, light in relation to their occupied volume, slippery and possessed of few flat surfaces. They are stacked three high, with scrap timber between the layers, intended to provide some grip when they are tightly and expertly roped down. The tarpaulin is not, of course, for weather protection, but as an extra precaution against pans falling off. This load has arrived in the classic condition, with pans loose inside on all four sides of the vehicle. Which side will the driver open? He is obviously not a complete beginner, for he backs his horse quite neatly to get one side of the wagon hard up against the wall of the shed. Next, he scrounges some dunnage bags through the good offices of the shed clerk, and lays them along the other side. Now comes the moment of truth; as he slackens the rope at one rear corner a bulge at the middle of the top begins to migrate ominously, but our man is equal to the challenge, and to the intense disappointment of the audience he controls the tension on the rope so that the delinquent pan slides gently down the inside of the tarpaulin until he can take hold of it and extract it. This process is repeated four times, until he is at last able to roll the sheet back over the top to the wall and inform the clerk that his load is ready for the dock labourers to stow in the shed, where it will wait for the next boat for Muirtown.

Outside, the comings and goings on the tide are nearly over: everything that was in the dock early this morning has gone now, with the exception of the Belfast boat, the *Pigeon*, the weevilly grain, and the two flats 'awaiting orders'. In their places have arrived another Dublin boat, another rubbish boat, two tramps from the west coast of Wales, and one of the Board's grab dredgers which has arrived in response to complaints made a couple of weeks ago about a build-up of mud in the north-east corner. There is also a most unusual arrival for William Dock, in the shape of a topsail schooner from Porthmadoc,[11] laden with slates for the new transit sheds which are being built just to the north, and, it is rumoured, for a new roof on the west shed here. The gatemen are waiting to close the passage gates, for the tide is already well turned, but their list shows a Northwich boat still due with a cargo of soda-ash. The piermaster arrives and tells them to close up: the packet has been sighted, still barely visible by telescope, little below Ellesmere Port, and even with the help of the ebb it will be at least another half hour. They will keep the river gates open longer, but if he does not arrive quickly he will have to anchor until the night tide.

Close to the end of the east shed is a cocoa-van operated by the British Working Men's Temperance Society,[12] and among the customers standing round it is a man who looks like an ageing Bob Cratchet. His dress is quite as formal in style as that of the corn arbitrator, but is of inferior quality and great age. He is the travelling timekeeper from the Engineer's Department, and he has come to log the hours worked by the men who repaired the swing bridge and the men on the dredger which has just arrived. His cocoa-drinking and his shabby respectability are, in fact, a carefully studied mask. He enquires as to the whereabouts of the bridge men, and is told they have gone to lunch. He actually knows this perfectly well, as he also knows that lunch comes in heavy ironic inverted commas. The bridge gang have finished work for the day, and will spend the afternoon where they are now, namely in the Arcadia opposite the gate. With a studied sigh which indicates how unhappy is the lot of a travelling timekeeper, he proceeds to that most inappropriately named hostelry. Inside, the bridge gang are well established in a corner, and have annexed the only table in the room. On it, by an empty stool, stands a substantial glass of best Trinidad. Enter our timekeeper, who without a glance at anyone in the room, sits on the stool, empties the glass of Trinidad, and takes out his pocket notebook. Another glass of Trinidad materializes, and a performance begins which makes the Biblical unjust steward look more than a trifle naive. The lad from the gang is worried: what if the head timekeeper should catch them there, after all, they are in a most obvious place, the nearest pub to where they are meant to be working. Patiently, the timekeeper explains to the lad that he knows which pubs the head timekeeper goes in, and vice versa. If they did not stick to that routine there would be a chance of their meeting accidentally, and that would cause embarrassment. The lad is still not convinced: might not the piermaster or the dockmaster come in, looking for men of his who were not where they should be? With great patience, over the fourth glass of Trinidad, the pubs are enumerated in which each and every clique and sub-species of dock worker is to be found, and when. If it did not work like that, then how would the piermaster know where to find a few extra men in an emergency? What would happen if a river gate failed and you needed a gang of shipwrights in a hurry? Gradually it becomes clear to the lad that the pubs are not only the place where much of the corruption of dock work takes place – such as that in which they are engaged – but are also an important channel of communication.

The door opens, and fourteen assorted men and boys enter. They are the majority of the dredger crew, who have come in to book their hours. More glasses of Trinidad, more fiction in the notebook. One seeks confidentiality, which is granted, and explains that he has an unexpected medical bill to pay, and needs a loan. A bag of sovereigns is produced, and a loan agreed 'at the usual rate'. How much of the money for the medical bill will survive the forthcoming session is open to doubt, but the power of the timekeeper's office makes his risk a minimal one, and moralizing he happily leaves to Holy Joe. He will go home tonight with a clear conscience, knowing that if he and his kind did not behave as they do, the whole administrative system of the docks would collapse.[13]

The dock policeman enters. He has been keeping an eye on a shady character who is selling tobacco which he clearly did not acquire honestly. There is a difference between tobacco which has been stolen out of a bonded warehouse and tobacco which has been received as a bribe or through falsifying damage records on a salvage job. The constable wishes to ensure that this is not a case of what he regards as legitimate perks, and on being assured that no one in the Engineer's Department has 'salvaged' any tobacco since a flat with a transfer cargo for Birkenhead sank in dock five weeks ago, goes on his genial way to arrest the malefactor.

On his way back, he discovers that two women have slipped past his colleague at the gate. Three kinds of women do this: bona fide wives or friends of crews of vessels in the dock, but they usually introduce themselves, prostitutes in search of custom among the crews, who are not welcome because they attract the attention of do-gooders who might learn too much, and scavengers. These women are of the latter kind, and our constable knows exactly where he will find them. Alongside the rubbish wharf is a makeshift incinerator consisting of the up-ended firebox of a steam crane boiler. Its specific purpose is to burn rubbish which might attract scavengers, such as scrap wood, condemned ropes and sacks. The practice began almost as soon as the dock was built, and was well-intentioned in the sense that docks are dangerous places where women should not be picking through rubbish. But few of the police see it that way, and the gatekeepers, whose job includes burning the rubbish, are markedly slow to burn anything that looks like good firewood. Sure enough, that is where he finds the two shawlies. He informs them that taking firewood from the docks is larceny, and that a Birkenhead man was recently gaoled for three months for stealing little more than a pocketful of scrap iron, and that he has to walk round the dock, which takes twelve minutes. The message is understood: as soon as his back is turned a knife is produced and a few yarns cut from a bit of scrap rope, some wood is bundled and in ten minutes there is no sign of wood or shawlies.[14]

On the bridge, an elderly man propels a huge sweeping brush which retains nearly a dozen bristles. On an average day several hundred horses pass over some part of the quays and roadways around the dock, and the evidence of their passing is gathered up by contract quay-sweepers. The contractor for whom this man works is the widow of a Board stonemason who was killed in an accident some years ago. The dock Charitable Fund had dealt generously with her, and her late husband had been a well-paid and thrifty man, so she was able to invest in the lease of a small patch of land alongside the canal in Lightbody Street, and a horse and cart. She had no trouble in securing a contract from the Board on the recommendation of a dockmaster who had been a friend of her husband, and she now pays a small amount to the Board for the privilege of removing manure, which is carted to her yard and heaped up until there is a boatload, when it is taken to Lathom Wharf and sold to local farmers. She will never be rich, but she has done well enough that the little capital she started with has been re-instated and she now has two horses and carts and employs six men. The man we are observing is of huge stature and, when he pauses from sweeping and stands straight, it is obvious that he has been a fine physical specimen. But he straightens only to draw breath for paroxysms of coughing. It does not require the talents of the Master Sleuth of Baker Street to recognize a superannuated corn porter.

On the far side of the bridge, a gateman is sitting on a capstan, soaking wet, wrapped in a blanket and drinking rum from a tin cup. The reason he looks so happy after immersion in very cold and very dirty water is that he has just rescued the cabin boy of the *Pigeon*, who was grappling for lost gear in the corner of the dock (contrary to bye-law) and fell in. It is virtually automatic that unless several reliable witnesses testify that our gatekeeper pushed him in he will be awarded £2 10s from the Charitable Fund, the going rate for rescuing a non-swimmer. [15]

A grinding noise behind the east shed indicates that a long-standing source of friction is about to be removed. Nearly three weeks ago, the LNWR delivered fifty or so tons of pig-iron scrap for use as ballast in a small Irish sailing vessel which had discharged a cargo of potatoes, and was to collect its outward cargo from Mostyn Dock on the Dee. The problem is that the potatoes were actually discharged in Salthouse Dock, and the ballast has been lying here in everyone's way ever since. In much the same way that the Board and its committees have bitter clashes with the railway companies before Royal Commissions, so their employees feud at every level from general manager downwards. This pile of ballast nearly caused a serious incident, when a railway shunter was attacked, and his wages stolen and a rumour started that his assailants had been quayside labourers from this berth. A considerable number of railway workers was gathering to exact retribution when it was revealed by the piermaster, who confronted them, that two contract shipwrights who had been working at Clarence Graving Dock had been arrested and charged with the offence, that the motive appeared to be simple robbery, and that the men were due to appear before the magistrates the next morning.[16]

Now, at last, one of the railway company's large stable of shires has arrived with four extremely disreputable small flat wagons in tow, with eight rather sour-looking men riding (contrary to bye-law) on them, and two substantial hand-trucks. The face of a horse is not well adapted to a supercilious expression, but this one is trying as its chain traces are unhooked and it walks off towards the Waterloo Goods Depot whence it came. The eight men with the two trucks start removing the ballast, during the course of which it becomes clear why they have avoided the job for as long as they could: it is uncommonly awkward stuff to handle. Some iron ballast is specially made for the job, roughly cast of reject material, but of a shape which makes it easy to stack and handle. This is not: it is of irregular shape and size and the weight of the pieces varies from about half a hundredweight to about two hundredweight. It has no handholds, no easy way of attaching a rope or a hook and some of the edges are broken and sharp. There is much grunting and heaving and a fair amount of indelicate language, especially from one who splits the end of his finger. The trucks have small cast iron wheels which run with an enormous amount of free play on iron axles which have had about a third of their diameter worn away from the bottom upwards, so that they gain something like a mind of their own as they bump over the cobbles. When they eventually finish and wend their ill-tempered way back to their depot, the problem of the ballast will not be at an end, for the wagons are on the same siding as those at the back of the east shed and are blocking them in. It will take a number of rancorous messages spread over two days before a locomotive will appear to take away the ballast and the empty wagons from behind the shed, and it will only arrive when the railway company needs to get another part-cargo to the Belfast boat. While they were working, they did not notice the slight glint from the top of the clock tower, but the piermaster was watching them through his telescope, for he knew that surplus ballast has a habit of 'accidentally' falling in the dock, and few things would give him greater pleasure than a bye-law prosecution of railway employees. It would cause even greater amusement to the quayside workers, who had debated whether they ought not to claim the ballast as their work – at overtime rates, of course – but decided that it was such a nasty little job that the railway men were welcome to it.

The Northwich packet arrived just in time to get into Salisbury, among some harsh comments from the gatemen, who should have been in the canteen by now, and the dockmaster decides that there is so little depth in Salisbury, through holding the gates for her, that he will not re-open the passage to William until the tide is rising again.[17] While this does not please her skipper, his crew are less than heartbroken when they learn that once they have unbattened the hatch-covers there is nothing further they can usefully do for about six hours. They never mind having time spare at William Dock, for the canteen is far better than any of the facilities on the Weaver. Like many of the estuarial crews, they keep a small terrier on board, and a further benefit of William Dock is that just up the road is the last pub in Liverpool which still holds rat-killing competitions. Their dog is highly proficient, and they normally emerge having imbibed liberally and still showing a shilling or two profit. Occasionally they drink enough for sentimental liberality to induce them to purchase a meat pie on the way back by way of payment to their little benefactor. Today, however, he will earn them nothing, for the rat-catcher is ill, and the supply of rats is barely sufficient for the evening session, so there will be no contest in the afternoon.[18]

By about 4.30 p.m. the light is beginning to fail in the sheds. Although it will be perfectly adequate for continued work outside for another couple of hours, the sun is getting low in the sky and the small skylights of the sheds gather but little from it. A lamplighter makes his way along the west shed, but the lamps he is lighting are oil lamps installed in 1845 and the difference they make is purely psychological. It has been possible for twenty years or more to obtain highly effective gas floodlights, and the Docks and Quays Committee has been experimenting in some places with the promising-looking electric lamps, but developments like that occur in more prestigious places than William Dock. Work in the sheds begins to wind down, and by 5.15 p.m. the last of the men working there has booked off and gone. The workers on the open quaysides continue a little longer, and the men at the rubbish wharf stay until 6.00 p.m. The dock goes quite quiet, as the only work which is still going on is that on board the various vessels and the lonely efforts of a coppersmith who arrived very late to repair the weather vane which stands on top of the gable end of the canteen. Only the Belfast boat is due out on the night tide, and she is already nearly fit to sail, but several inward-bound vessels are expected. The dockmaster finishes for the day, walking back to his rather grand residence at Princes entrance, while the piermaster, who will be on duty for the night tide goes to his flat in the clock tower for his customary and substantial high tea with his wife and a couple of hours' sleep. Normally he would not need to do this, but one of his two head gatemen is in hospital so he will have to take charge.

The lonely figure of the working dockman, who has just come on duty for a twelve-hour turn, approaches *Pigeon*, whose skipper has returned from a shopping trip to the city centre. He had obviously been upsetting his wife, for he was carrying a large box bearing the name of a Bold Street furrier of some repute as a costly peace-offering.[19] The working dockman has received a message that the vessel in Princes Graving Dock is coming out overnight, and is advising the skipper to be ready to move at 6.00 a.m., to dock when the shipwrights start work at 7.00 a.m. The skipper is not pleased by this news, for he had been told that he would not be able to dock for another day or two, and has no means of contacting the surveyor now, to try to get him to come sooner. His company will almost certainly have to pay for a longer stay in the dock than is really necessary, a misfortune which distresses the working dockman not at all, who enquires tenderly after the condition of *Pigeon*'s GS pump – a sarcastic comment on the rather poor job of deck-cleaning which has been done during the skipper's absence. He now climbs across to *Anna Marie*, where he finds the bosun still in charge, reclining in a hammock in the warmth of the engine room and reading a book of a kind which would raise Holy Joe to something over a hundred decibels. The boilers are banked and slacked, but consultation with the stoker confirms that there will be sufficient steam to use the deck winch to warp her out of the way and then back again. Little enthusiasm is expressed about the idea of getting up that early just to release *Pigeon*, and the dockman kindly suggests that if they wish they can move now and tie up outside the rubbish boat. The bosun knows what time the rubbish boatmen from the canal start work, and churlishly declines the offer, countering with the suggestion that the dredger might be a more congenial bedfellow on the grounds that her crew will be so overhung they are unlikely to make much noise before midday. Rather to his surprise, this suggestion is accepted, so the stoker opens his dampers a little, to replace the steam they will use, while the bosun goes to extract the one and only deck-hand from the forecastle. The said deck-hand is not happy: he is just completing major ablutions preparatory to yet another futile attempt at finding a nice girl who loves a sailor and is only pacified by the loan of the only pair of working gloves aboard, property of the absent engineer.

Anna Marie has her bow into the corner of the dock, and it is decided that she must be turned. The winch is warmed through again, and the rope paid out along the deck aft until it reaches to the starboard bollard of the dredger. A light rope is bent onto it near the drum, and the deck-hand goes ashore with this, to the corner by the bridge. More rope is paid out, which he pulls over a capstan idler by means of his handline, and the bosun lays the main rope through a fairlead on *Anna Marie*'s port bow. The rope thus forms a triangle, and when the bosun casts off forward and pulls very gently with the winch, the bow begins to swing out, the after mooring preventing the vessel from moving forwards. 'Cast off' and the deck-hand waits for a little slack in the rope, and whips it off the idler and allows it to fall in the water. The bosun carefully takes up the slack and continues to wind in, swinging the vessel round, using its own stem as a springer. When *Anna Marie* is diagonally against the stern of the dredger, a short line is temporarily used to hold her in that position while the winch rope is moved to the dredger's bow. The deck-hand now takes the aft mooring in hand, with two turns on the bollard, and further winching rolls *Anna Marie* on the fenders and brings her parallel to and alongside the dredger. The stoker lends a hand at the final stage, which is to get a temporary line from the stern bollard onto the dredger to serve until the line the deck-hand is using is freed from the quayside. This temporary line brings the vessel to a halt, enabling them to adjust their fenders and lines, leaving themselves an undisturbed evening of idleness and a good night's sleep.[20]

At this point we must leave William Dock. The time is already nearing when the first movements of the night tide will begin and the cycle will repeat itself. Some of those working here will reflect on the injustice of a world where the docks which have the largest number of comings and goings are never the ones which get the latest and best of the quayside lighting, and one, who is caught in the bight of a rope in the darkness and propelled into the dock will reflect on it at greater length, during a short stay in hospital. Over the return of the various revellers we will draw a veil, as also over what the bosun of *Anna Marie* will say when the dredger crew come to knock him up at 5.30 a.m. to get him to move.

CHAPTER NINE

THE FUTURE AS SEEN IN 1905

The popular image of Edwardian England is of a country enjoying the fruits of a century of world leadership in industry and commerce, blissfully unaware that in a few short years the whole golden autumnal pleasure of life would be inundated in the mud and blood of the Western Front, never to re-emerge. Visits to stately homes and to site museums pander to this view, as each vies with the others in portrayal of its own Edwardian heyday until one has to be careful to avoid lapsing into the belief that the Edwardian years were indeed the heyday of everyone and everything. An alternative perspective suggests that this was the heyday of capitalist exploitation in which the rich got richer and the poor got poorer.

A walk around the commercial centre of Liverpool will reinforce these views, the efforts at urban renewal by the *Luftwaffe* in the '40s and the City Council in the '60s notwithstanding. The majority of the office buildings which catch the eye for anything other than crass ugliness – whether for subtlety of design, fineness of detailing or just sheer size and extravagance, were designed and/or built between 1900 and 1914. Few things fit better with the popular image of Edwardian England than the bulk of the Royal Liver Building, or the lavish splendour of the dock offices. A little further afield, the towering mega-Gothic of Liverpool Cathedral was begun on a site donated by the City Council in 1903, the same year that the university received its Charter.

It is a dangerous thing to listen too often to 'Land of Hope and Glory', especially if it is forgotten that its most familiar version was not an expression of Edwardian smugness, it was a rework by a distinctly lukewarm Elgar for the British Empire Exhibition of 1924.

His tune 'such as comes once in a lifetime' first had words set to it in the Coronation Ode of 1910, a work whose libretto and music alike conceal amid their *nobilmente* patriotism a good deal of worry and self-doubt. The issues were far from clear cut.

So it was with the Dock Board. While some of the members were perfectly happy to sit back and thank the God who had made them mighty, trusting that He would continue to do His stuff, others certainly felt it necessary that they should 'ask of thyself, and see that thy sons be strong' for the problems their sons would have to face were not beyond a horizon on which only a golden sunset was visible, they were storm clouds which were nearly overhead.

At first glance, the Board seemed to be in an excellent position. The tonnage of shipping paying dues to the Board was continuing to rise, indeed it rose by nearly a quarter between 1900 and 1905. Within that total, some of the rise was in tonnage paying harbour dues only, i.e. vessels using other ports on the Mersey, principally those on the Manchester Ship Canal, but the greater part – over 2¾ million tons – was in vessels using the docks.[1] In terms of market share, Liverpool seemed to have turned the corner, for having suffered a small steady decline throughout the second half of the nineteenth century, her share of the recent national recovery in traffic was large. Between 1899–1903 (inclusive) the total increase in value of British imports and exports was 10.8 per cent, or in money terms £88.4 million. Of that, Liverpool accounted for £36.1 million or nearly 41 per cent. That share of growth was greater than those of London, Manchester, Glasgow, Bristol and Hull put together. The fact that revenues had not rocketed was simply due to the fact that the Board was a non-profit-making body, and when it was prospering it could and did cut rates to its customers; had traffic in 1904 been charged 1884 prices it would have placed another £427,000 in the Board's coffers.

The opening of the ship canal had made inroads into Liverpool's traditional staple traffic of cotton, but the indications were that its novelty was wearing thin. Averaged for each of the five years to 1903, Liverpool had handled between 74 and 78 per cent of all imports of cotton to Britain: in 1903 the share had leaped to 85 per cent. Another staple, the tobacco trade, was showing a gratifying return on investment in the huge Stanley Tobacco Warehouse, and a record total of 125,000 hogsheads was earning rent for the Board in 1904.

A more homespun indicator of the state of trade was also favourable, namely that Liverpool supplied more bunker coal to foreign bound steamers than any other port,[2] for as everyone knew, the more fuel you need, the more work was being done.

It may be that some members were worried by loss of some traffics: for example the grain trade had started to import at Hull and Grimsby on quite a large scale, and small obsolescent canal ports like Ellesmere Port and Goole were receiving heavy investment from the milling trade. Yet these must have seemed doomed ventures. The simplest and most observable shipping trend over the whole of the previous century had been the rise in the average size of ships, and in 1905 this trend could be seen not merely continuing but accelerating. In the Liverpool Boston trade, for example, the average ship in 1872 was of 3,337 tons and 362 ft length. By 1897 the tonnage had grown to 5,971 and the length to 468 ft, but by 1905 the increase had been to an amazing 12,213 tons and 561 ft. These figures had a very clear message: any port which did not cater for ever-larger ships was sooner or later doomed, and the probability, given the acceleration, was that it would be sooner. Liverpool had followed a consistent policy for decades of keeping up with rising ship size and even now, in 1905, was planning such a monster of a dock as would admit the super-dreadnoughts and Cunard *Queens* of the future. There was little need to worry about small and medium sized ports including Manchester, for they would be rendered obsolete: quite soon an average, as distinct from a large, ship would be unable to get there.

In the passenger trade, Liverpool's dominance was spectacular. In 1904, London, Southampton and Queenstown, the three next largest passenger ports, handled a total of 134,000 outward-bound passengers compared with Liverpool's 274,000. There was continuous pressure on the Board for extra berthing space for these gigantic vessels and for the larger and faster North Atlantic cargo liners, some of which were of comparable size with the lesser 'ocean greyhounds', and which arrived at the rate of fourteen per week. The Liverpool Steamship Owners Association, which owned 21 per cent of all British steam tonnage and 43 per cent of the number of larger vessels (those over 5,000 tons), was firmly in agreement with the Board's projected figures which indicated a growth of 2½ million tons over five years beginning 1906.[3]

As if all this were not enough, the Board was justifiably expecting a visit from Santa Claus. The tonnage figures quoted in the paragraphs above are net register tonnages, and it was by NRT that all the Board's charges were made. However NRT was no longer an accurate indication of the size or payload of a vessel, nor of the demands it made on dock facilities. In particular, passenger liners and the largest fastest classes of cargo liner had got to the point where their NRT could be as little as one third of their gross tonnage, and it was, of course, the GT which governed the size and depth of berth required. Because of this, quite modest cargo vessels whose NRT was little less than their GT could end up paying more dues than the huge and much more demanding steamers of the famous North Atlantic lines. The fact that this resulted in the 'bread and butter' ships subsidizing the glamour traffic was obviously of concern to some, but for our purposes here it is sufficient to remark that the Board could look at its respectable growth in tonnage figures and then point out that, because of changes in naval architecture, the true growth was actually much greater. In addition, of course, the Board should then have been getting more revenue from the greyhounds than it was. In both 1903 and 1904 they had introduced Bills in Parliament to enable an alteration in their authorized charges, such that although NRT would remain the basis, vessels whose NRT was less than half their GT would nevertheless be charged at half the GT. Both these Bills failed, but the Board could confidently and rightly assume that this obvious anomaly would eventually be righted, with rapid and beneficial effects on their finances and prospects.[4]

In 1902, a Royal Commission[5] had reported on the administration of the Port of London, and the evidence would, if taken at face value, establish beyond doubt that Liverpool was in marvellous shape. Witness after witness compared London unfavourably with Liverpool, in terms of administrative efficiency, general quality of service to the shipowners, and above all speed of turn-round. Miles Burton, general manager and secretary of MDHB was called as a witness to reveal some of the secrets of the Board's success, and one small passage from his evidence is worth quoting in full for the impression of success it conveys:

4652. In fact, from a financial point of view, you are in clover? That is so.
4653. You have as much money as ever you want? Yes.

4654. Have you any complaints from persons on the other side, who pay your dues and charges, that these are too high? No.

As we shall see, all three of these statements were untrue, and the only reason they escaped unchallenged was that the enquiry was into the state of London, which was indeed demonstrably much worse than that of Liverpool. The third answer is particularly gross: shipowners always complained about everything, and their evidence to this commission was no exception. But it had gone down as a matter of public record that the Board was financially 'in clover'. There were definite reasons for making such claims, which those who thought the Board was financially in a cow-pat would find hard to disprove. Even Mountfield and Hyde, who fully recognized that the Board was suffering relative decline, seem to have been deceived by these and statements like them into believing that the port's decline was a cause for, as Holt put it, anxiety but little more.

It is, however, only fair to remark that had the boot been on the other foot, the evidence would have been reversed. Witnesses would have been found to explain how poor were the depths over the sills of Liverpool Docks, how few the hydraulics cranes and hoists, how iniquitous the master porterage system and how extortionate the charges. London would have emerged as the vision of an ideal port. The reality is, of course, that both ports were winning a declining share of the market, both were having trouble raising funds to keep abreast of the investment required and both were hindered by a management system which had grown by accretion.

When members of the shipowning community charged the Board with lethargy and inaction, as they often did, their accusations needed to be taken with a pinch of salt. They were, after all, in the business of finding the cheapest and best facilities they could to provide profits for their shareholders, and playing off one port against another was well within the rules of the game. There may have been valid complaints against the Board in 1905, but inaction was certainly not one of them. At the last Board meeting of 1904, held on 15 December, Robert Gladstone gave a round-up of the main developments during the year. The site of the new dock which would eventually be named after him had been partly prepared by the removal and dumping at sea of over a million cubic yards of spoil. The Brocklebank Dock and its passages had been deepened, its

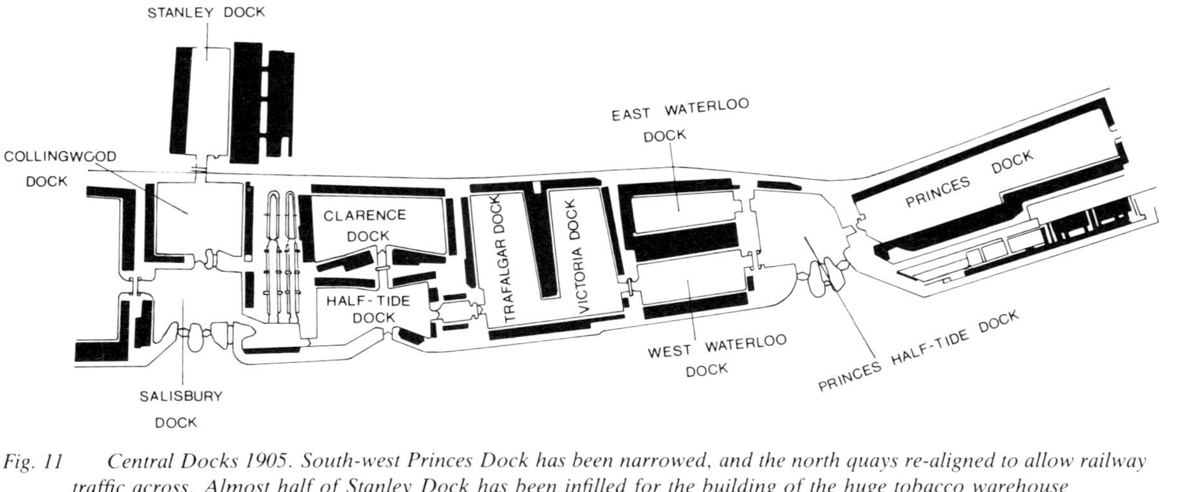

Fig. 11 *Central Docks 1905. South-west Princes Dock has been narrowed, and the north quays re-aligned to allow railway traffic across. Almost half of Stanley Dock has been infilled for the building of the huge tobacco warehouse*

graving dock was almost complete and work had started on the new branch No. 3. At Sandon, the deepening which went with the new entrances and the new half-tide dock had been completed, and a new two-storey transit shed was in use. The flour mill built by Rigby's at Waterloo had been completed, and the works on the west quay of Princes were in hand. The new dock offices were progressing rapidly, with five hundred men at work. In the South Docks, the new deep-water branches at Kings were in hand, while Queens No. 2 branch, with its two-storey sheds, had been completed. Coburg was being provided with a deep through channel to allow communication between those berths and the newly completed Brunswick entrances and five million tons of silt had been removed from the vicinity to allow deep-draughted vessels access to all these works. In the meantime, work was also proceeding on the Birkenhead side, and on the Board's land in Tranmere Bay. Any suggestion of inaction made from outside the Board could with perfect justice be dismissed as the product of total ignorance.

It is well known that statistics can be used to prove anything, and in 1905, as today, there was a choice of conclusions to which one could come before selecting the statistics to prove them. In the City Council in October 1904, Sir William Forwood made a speech which roused an immense and immediate controversy. The issue under discussion was a proposal that the Corporation ought to construct a number of light railways for goods traffic, to operate in a manner analogous to its extraordinarily successful system of electric trams. It was not, however, the strictures on the mainline railway companies which started the controversy, but the remark, made almost in passing, that 'He felt himself that Liverpool, situated as it was today, was a decaying city'. He subsequently admitted that 'decaying' was perhaps an oratorical excess and that 'stagnating' or similar might have been a better word. Such distinctions had become immaterial from the moment he uttered the original words. Some members of the Board and various apologists of theirs produced arguments such as those given above to show that far from Liverpool decaying, it was rapidly growing and probably at an increasing rate. But Forwood himself had already pointed out that tonnage figures could be misleading, for they related to the tonnage of the vessel, as well as to the goods it carried. There was a shipping tonnage surplus at the time, and many ships arrived in or left from Liverpool with part-cargoes.[6] One satirical gentleman had even described the operations of the Liverpool ballast trade, which he considered highly important to the well-being of the port. Another critic, described as a 'well-known sailing ship owner' not only agreed that the increased tonnage was 'largely empty' but also pointed out that a lot of it consisted of a relatively small number of large fast ships coming and going very frequently. In other traffics there was no increase at all, but a decrease. J.S. Dickey-Sam Jun., opined in the correspondence column of the *Liverpool Mercury* that there was a known decline in the traffic of the main railways in and out of Liverpool, which would suggest that whatever the Board and its NRT figures said, the actual quantities of goods were smaller.[7]

Arguments such as these were not too difficult for the optimists to counter. What did it matter which ships brought trade through the port, or how large or small, fast or slow, frequent or infrequent they were? What mattered was tonnage of goods and numbers of passengers, and both were rising. To suggestions of empty tonnage the Board could and did reply that if so much tonnage was empty it was indeed curious that the monetary value of the supposedly declining quantity of goods kept increasing. Where the traffic went from the Board's quays was immaterial: if it was not travelling by rail it was either travelling some other way or dematerializing: either way it seemed quite healthy until after it had paid its dues.

These arguments certainly sounded persuasive at the time, at least to some. Yet we can see that they were not entirely true, or indeed necessarily sincere, if we look back to the Central Docks. The new works at Princes west quay were good so far as they went, which was about half way: the north end of the west quay remained as an extempore and piecemeal arrangement based on the 1843 closed sheds and the 1872 'neo-Hartley' open sheds, while the whole length of the east side was lined with Hartley open sheds and the four short quays at the ends were equally obsolete. There was no power-operated handling equipment at all. On the east side the wall-batter remained until 1929, rendering 1,500 ft of quay highly inconvenient for the biggest and best coastal vessels. In short, the job at Princes was making the best of a shoe-string, and if the situation was really as good as the argument above might suggest, then it is legitimate to ask why only a shoe-string should be available.[8]

The answer might be, of course, as it had been in the early 1890s that there were so many more pressing works needed elsewhere for

Fig. 12 *All steel roof trusses,* c. *1900, as used in Princes Dock west shed*

more profitable traffics carried in larger vessels that the Central Docks would just have to wait. It is true that major improvements were still needed to deal with the problems of inadequate depth in the so-called 'deepwater docks', some of which were not. Equally, the coasting trade generated very little direct revenue for the Board. Towards the end of 1905, however, the Board discussed a further scheme for improvements in the Central Docks, this time at Clarence. The last significant improvements at Clarence are mentioned in the engineer's report for 1852, and its condition in 1905 was justifiably described by Mr Holt as 'miserable'. From such photographs as survive, this would appear to be an understatement: Clarence was more outdated in 1905 than the Old Dock had been when it was infilled in 1826. The new scheme involved a new entrance, which would not only improve access for deeper and squarer vessels, but would also enable the closure of Clarence and Salisbury entrances, both of which were still hand-operated and therefore highly extravagant in manpower as well as inadequate in size and depth. It was estimated that there would be a saving of £750 p.a. in the wages of the harbourmaster's department and the maintenance of one modern entrance as compared with two rather

Who is the author to disagree with Mr Holt, who described these facilities as 'miserable'?
(NMGM)

careworn ones would probably save a similar sum in the Engineer's Department.[9] The proposed new dock was to take vessels from the small ocean-going down to the largest coastal: vessels of this class were using Nelson Dock among others, to a constant chorus of complaints from their owners. Nelson, however, would provide comparatively splendid facilities for the vessels now using Clarence. Princes, despite its recently completed improvements, was considered barely adequate.

The discussion proceeded along lines which were to some extent predictable: the revenue from the coasting trade was so small that it would not meet the interest payments on this scheme, much less provide a return on the capital of nearly £750,000 involved. To this, others responded that the present facilities were so bad it was scarcely surprising that the revenue was low, and that investment was essential to retain traffic and to win back that which had demonstrably been lost. Remarks were made to the effect that money had been spent for the benefit of the coasting trade at Nelson and Princes 'and so on' (though it is difficult to identify the 'so on') and that the owners ought to be counting their blessings instead of whingeing about being neglected. This called forth from Mr Read the most perceptive remark of the meeting: 'It is not that you have neglected

This is what sheds were meant to be like at the turn of the century
(NMGM)

the coasting trade but that you have neglected your own estate in these Central Docks.' The Board was above comparing itself with smallfry, but if it had been willing to do so it would have realized that Garston and Ellesmere Port had significant works planned and even Runcorn and Weston Point had undergone modernization much more recently than Clarence, Collingwood or Salisbury. Even if it were logical to assess the results of the deepwater docks by comparison only with a handful of the largest ports, disregarding the leakage of small amounts of trade to various small ports, it certainly was not logical in the case of the coasting trade.

The Board, of course, knew this even if they would not admit it in so many words, for one of their favourite subjects for a good grumble was the ownership of dock facilities by railway companies. The evidence suggests that these grumbles were justified, for it would be surprising if the railway companies did not employ their rates structures to favour their own facilities, which is exactly what they did. But the traffic of which the Board complained they were being robbed was not going to London, Bristol, Glasgow or any other of the ports with which the Board made comparisons: it was going to places like Garston, Fleetwood and Heysham, which did not feature in the comparisons. In terms of the figures the Board quoted, therefore, a lot of traffic 'disappeared' for statistical purposes. Nor were all the railway-owned ports particularly small: alongside little ventures like Silloth there were rather larger ones like Barrow, Grimsby or Fishguard. Leaving aside the rather unrealistic option of the Board constructing its own mainline railways, there were two ways it could strike back, both of which related to the Central Docks, and both of which were ignored.

There was a major investigation into the state of canal transport in 1883. The principal features found in common between it and the Royal Commission of 1907–10 are that a great deal of time was spent listening to evidence from disgruntled railway users who wished to see canals enlarged and modernized in order to offer effective competition with railways, and that no action resulted. There was certainly some feeling in Liverpool that canal development would be a good idea; in an interview with the *Liverpool Post and Mercury* of 2 December 1904 George Cox, vice chairman of the Chamber of Commerce remarked that 'Since 1879 France has spent 100 million sterling on waterways and is now engaged in work involving a further

20 million; while Germany and Austria are spending 10 and 31 million respectively.' This was a follow-up to Sir Alfred Jones' opinion, expressed in an interview in the same paper on 5 November 1904 that 'One thing Liverpool ought to do is to endeavour to get cheap canal transit out of the port . . .' While the Board as a body might have found it hard to raise the money for major enlargement of the Leeds and Liverpool or other canals, there is no doubt that Liverpool contained enough men like Sir Alfred who were both rich and disgruntled that something could have been done – if only the canals had been seen as an effective weapon to wield against the common enemy. In fact, we find that the Board was far from helpful over canal boats loading and discharging cargoes overside to and from ships. Clearly they had a small-time and short-term interest in this, in that use of ship's tackle for such purposes meant that money was not being paid for the use of Board appliances, and was not providing a return on the investment represented therein, but it is hard to see why they could not take a wider view. One reason, perhaps, was that they still liked to think of their docks as being for ships rather than grubby little boats, which really ought not to be messing around wasting the time of the harbourmaster's department in looking after them. In short, it was another manifestation of the old delusion that docks are for ships, when in fact they are for goods. What is important is to understand the underlying logic of Sir Alfred's view: he did not say, nor probably did he imagine, that canals could offer a nationwide threat to the great railway system. What they could do, and should have been enabled to do, was to muscle in on the large-volume short-haul traffics like that between Liverpool and the Lancashire cotton towns to sufficient effect that the railway companies, instead of using those routes to subsidize others, would have to use other routes to subsidize rates which could compete with canal transport. On their previous record the railway companies would have been tempted to adopt this tactic, which had caused huge damage to the canal industry in the past – but they would have been faced with an awful dilemma over rates to their own ports. In which foot should they decide to shoot themselves? A programme by the Board of providing enhanced facilities for canal boats, backed by improved access for bigger boats via Stanley as well as a concerted campaign by local commercial heavyweights for investment in the canal could have caused some severe headaches in

railway circles, and the chance of doing that was identified – but missed.

A more basic failing seems to have been that the Board did not realize that coastal shipping was a second, and potentially more potent, way of striking back at the railway interest. Members persisted in viewing coastwise trade as shipping rather than as a distributive function of the port. Their frequent suggestions that investment should depend on revenue from dues on coasters is evidence of this misunderstanding. No one suggested that railway wagons or carts on the road should pay dock dues on their tonnage, yet coasters were just as vital a part of the gathering and distribution of goods on which the whole trade of the port depended. Not only that, but coasters were the most likely means of providing effective competition against the railways, particularly on some of their most expensive routes, such as the West Coast mainline to Glasgow. If coastal trade really only contributed £38,000 per year to the port, was it worth the trouble of collecting it? As Sir Alfred put it, 'In fact I don't see why it would not pay Liverpool to let the coasters come into the port free, to relieve and feed the big ocean liners . . . the coasting trade is entirely a helpmeet to the ocean liners, and they should be encouraged in every possible way.'[10] If it was true, as Sir William Forwood alleged, that 'the railways were strangling the port' then at least two opportunities of doing something about them had been allowed to go begging. But the railway companies had been the bogeyman for so long that it is hard to rely on such a routine applause-winner inserted in a speech.

Outside of the Board, there was no shortage of critics. Some of them had, like Sir William or Sir Alfred, specific complaints or suggestions. Others, either through a more dogmatic nature or through having been driven to despair, suggested more radical alterations. 'A prominent member of the Steamship Owners Association' explained to the *Mercury* on 9 November 1904 how the Board had made various mistakes which ought to be rectified, of which one was the building of the warehouses. The awful situation of the present could be rectified by abolishing the Board and handing the docks back to a new Dock Committee.[11] Such an argument must have cheered the Board considerably, for it showed the level of knowledge of their critics – or at least could be said to. Of the warehouses the Board owned, two were fairly prosperous, the rest were not: the former were those built by the Board (Waterloo and Stanley Tobacco) and the others were built by that Dock Committee whose revival would supposedly cure all ills. But this logic did not prevent an extraordinary proposal to the City Council on 10 November 1904 to the effect that the Council should invest in the construction of docks of small to medium size on the stretch of foreshore between Herculaneum and Garston. More extraordinary than the proposal itself was the fact that twenty-four members voted for it, losing only by nine votes, which may serve as an indication of the discontent which the Board's treatment of smaller ships aroused.

It did not help the Board that there were at the time five hundred men working on their new head office building, the design for which had emerged from a competition announced in 1899. The rules for competitors made it quite clear that a building of some grandeur was required: 'Competitors are not restricted as to the style of the building, but its exterior and interior must be dignified, as befitting its purpose.' The Board Room of the old building in Canning Place was 34 ft 10 in by 31 ft 4 in by 18 ft 10 in high, 'but it is thought that these dimensions might be increased with advantage.' Dignity of purpose

Was this shameless extravagance, or a rather clever bluff? The new Dock Offices under construction, probably 1906

(NMGM)

clearly did not extend to customers, for the Graving Dock office was to have a counter about 20 ft long with 'seating for four clerks and about fifty public (which was what the Board called paying customers) waiting'. The members, on the other hand, had seven committee clerks, each with three assistants. It is hardly surprising that such a building, embarked upon at a cost of over a quarter of a million pounds, should arouse some resentment among 'public'.[12] An interview with 'a prominent James Street shipowner' in the *Journal of Commerce* for 26 October 1904 accuses the Board of extravagance and suggests that had they managed their estate prudently Liverpool might have been practically a free port instead of one of the dearest in the kingdom. 'The money spent on new dock offices should have gone in reduction of the dock dues.' Here we see a critic who has not only let his judgement be clouded by the fact that he is jealous of someone else's smart new office, but who has not even realized where the money allegedly wasted ought to be going, namely in improved facilities rather than enhancing the short-term profits of shipowners so that they could afford nice new desks for their principals.

The evidence so far could be taken as suggesting that the Board was operating on at least a fairly sound footing and could thus look forward to reaping the benefits of major investment in dock improvement as well as to revenues which would suffice to continue the programme. Against the loss of some traffics to small and medium sized ports could be set the likelihood that continued growth in ship size would render such losses decidedly temporary. The criticisms advanced are mostly those of sectional interests, not necessarily very well informed ones: the only charge which seems to stick is that relating to the need to foster canals or the coastal trade as a means of competition with railways. That is at least partly what the proposed improvements at Clarence were about, and Holt, who had long advocated improvements in the Central Docks (since at least 1890) was a consistent opponent of the railway interests: his arguments in favour of this latest scheme are no foible, nor are they a pursuit of his own interests outside the Board. With such arguments, and such a protagonist, in their favour, how could the improvements fail to gain approval for the smallish sum of three-quarters of a million pounds?

Historically, the Board had raised funds for construction and improvement by the issue of bonds, nearly all of which were taken up locally. In answer to a passing question about land purchase,

A.G. Lyster said of Mr Muspratt 'I do not know whether he has got any of our bonds or not – most people in Liverpool have.'[13] This method of raising funds had the advantage of convenience through business done verbally on 'Change' and of keeping funds within the Liverpool mercantile community and thus available for reinvestment, but the disadvantage was that it was costly, with typical rates of 4 per cent; Debenture stocks or other loans secured on property typically paid 3½ per cent or less. The Board had never held powers to issue such stocks, because, like the Dock Committee before them, they had been quite happy with the existing system. By the time the Board wished to change (which was as early as 1898) Liverpool was no longer full of capital swilling around in search of investment opportunities. Those same large ships which gave the Board such confidence in the future had absorbed amazing amounts of local capital, by no means all of which was providing generous returns owing to oversupply of tonnage. Some of the most innovative local entrepreneurs had invested heavily in plant overseas for such things as chilling chickens in China. Members of the Board both corporately and individually had mocked the possibility of the Manchester Ship Canal ever raising its enabled capital, and they were in a sense proven right, for the canal owed its construction to a rescue operation by Manchester City Council. The result was that when the Board finally attempted to issue a redeemable 3 per cent stock in 1900 there was a marked shortage of takers and only £92,000 out of an authorized £5 million was issued. The Boer War and its aftermath made a further attempt in the immediate future inadvisable, and by 1904 the situation had become extremely serious. It was not simply a case of revenue leaking away in overhigh interest payments, though estimates were that a properly funded debt would save between £100,000 and £200,000 per year,[14] there were also large numbers of bonds falling due for repayment. In the July quarter of 1905, repayments had amounted, with interest, to over £1 million, and of the Board's total debt of £22½ million about £20 million fell due within the next ten years. Furthermore, major capital works aside, the debt was increasing at the rate of about half a million pounds per year. Such a situation was verging on crisis status, and the time for issuing a stock was, if anything, less opportune than ever. The Russo-Japanese war had absorbed a great deal of capital, and a Russian Government stock issue of £24½ million was imminent: the Board's expectation was that the rate and/or discount offered on that would reflect the desperate need of Russia to keep its war effort going, and that it would thus soak up available money. This not only forced them into going to London, for the first time, to raise money, but to consider paying a higher rate than they would have liked. A further portion of humble pie came their way in negotiations with their London agents as the realization dawned on them that they had no hope of a par issue succeeding and might have to discount by as much as 6 per cent.

The purpose of this digression into finance is to show that even if the Board had some surviving delusions of grandeur, it had by 1905 been brought face to face with reality. When critics outside the Board levelled accusations of 'a false pride' they did so without the benefits of minutes of Board meetings from which reporters were excluded. Had they heard Mr Parker, chairman of the Finance Committee, state that 'one way or another we shall need about £3½ million between now and this time next year' and that 'In the meantime our financial necessities are such that we cannot longer delay the situation . . .' they might have written differently. The Board was also perfectly aware that Edwardian England was not the lovely stable place so often portrayed: Mr Rome, when considering the best time for the Board to float its stock, remarked that 'after the experience of these two wars (the Boer War and the Russo-Japanese) there will be less chance of another war during the next eight or ten years.' That was a sufficiently astute guess to suggest that the Board's crystal ball was in reasonable working order.[15]

Saddled with debt and with the 'sow's ear', together with the 'miserable' Central Docks, what could the Board do? The answer seems to have been that they would make a last desperate throw, and back their judgement on the growing need for ever larger docks. By the time the 1904/5 crisis broke, they had already acquired and partly prepared the site for Gladstone Dock. They did not have the money to build it; indeed at the time the decision to go to Parliament was made they did not have the money to remain in business long-term. In the event, their judgements were proved correct, and however persuasive the logic of spending money on the Central Docks may have seemed then, or seems now, they succeeded in extricating themselves from a seemingly impossible situation not only solvent but with the powers and the funds to build their giant new dock. Their idea that rising ship sizes would cripple some smaller competitors (and there was, of course, one in particular they would not mind seeing crippled) looked too far ahead, for it was another giant new dock built as one more last desperate throw and opened in 1972, which achieved that, but in almost every other respect they were proved right.

It may be thought that if the Board had indeed shed any delusions of grandeur it may have had, then in two respects it showed little sign of it. One was construction of the new offices, but it must be remembered that these were undertaken against a background of long-standing problems with the old office building in Canning Place, which was overcrowded, deficient in terms of washing and lavatory provision (especially for 'Lady Typewriters') and generally in a poor state of repair. The money spent on the new offices was not, as critics alleged, from dock revenues, but from the happy windfall of a sale of land to the City Council for their Pier Head improvement scheme.

The potentially more damaging accusation of extravagance related to *Galatea*. In 1895, the Board had purchased an elderly, but rather elegant, paddle steamer called *Galatea* for £3,000. It was intended for carrying members around for inspections of the outstations and lightships of the Board and for general service as a VIP tender. Such activities might well be open to criticism as 'junketing', and the early service record of the vessel was fairly unhappy as well. Within months of her acquisition it was discovered that she needed reboilering at a cost of over £2,200 and various modifications, including the fitting of steam steering gear were undertaken. In November 1896 it was found that her intermediate crankshaft was of insufficient strength to meet Board of Trade requirements, with the result that her boiler pressure was reduced to 32 lb/in^2 (rather than fit a new and larger shaft) to make her comply. In October 1904 the Marine Committee was informed that she required serious expenditure if she was to pass survey for a renewal of her passenger certificate and on 28 November the advice was that this work was not worth undertaking. Accordingly, in January 1905, it was decided that a new vessel 'to be fitted out in the same manner as a first class passenger ship' should be ordered. This new vessel, which was to cost £20,075, was ordered four days after the financial agonizing described above was at its height. What sort of organization could wring its hands over a terrible financial situation while squandering money on a floating freeloading parlour?[16]

The old Galatea *in Wallasey Dock*

(NMGM)

Had this accusation been levelled at the Board, which it appears it was not, their response would doubtless have been that *Galatea* did far more than ferry members around. It was a dual-purpose vessel, equipped to replace not only its direct predecessor but also the old survey vessel, and it was also hired out quite frequently to other organizations for a wide variety of purposes, many of which might be considered to be directed towards 'opinion formers' from outside the area, thus fulfilling a PR function for the Board at the same time as earning revenue. While this justification may have been tolerably well founded, it was not altogether complete or sincere. The Board needed, in the foreseeable future, to raise something of the order of £20 million to stabilize its long-term finances. Then there was another £12 million for the new dock, and of these sums about £4 million was needed very soon. It is well known that loans are only available to those that do not need them, and if the Board intended, as it did, to go to the City for very large sums of money, then it needed to live up to the picture of prosperity that some of the statistics presented. To be seen to pension off a high profile vessel like the old *Galatea*, which was, after all, nearing forty years old, and not replace it, would create suspicion and might result in the ultimate disaster of another failed stock issue. Measured against a risk such as that, the spending of £20,000 was a sprat to catch a mackerel. If it saved the need for a discount of only $\frac{1}{4}$ per cent on the stock, then it would represent a net gain of about £60,000.

The main question about the Central Docks is how they managed to fester in a little island of neglect when everything around them was modernized. The need for modernization really became acute by about 1870, and that was the time when a purpose built highly-mechanized coastal terminal should have been built, based on them. The need at the time was pressing for bigger docks for bigger ships, which might understandably delay works on coastal facilities. It was the failure of the works under the 1873 Act to achieve anything approaching the capacity for which they were intended which threw the Board into three decades of piecemeal alterations and improvements aimed at achieving those objectives. The result was a climate in which accommodation of big ships was always first on the agenda and a financial situation where the money ran out before the meeting proceeded to the consideration of Item 2. When Clarence Dock was finally infilled, it was not so much obsolete as a fascinating time capsule, despite being a supposedly operational dock, and it is certainly arguable that if the coasting trade had not been expected to operate in facilities like that, it might have remained more competitive for longer. That Clarence was allowed to remain unmodernized until 1928 was not, however, the result of neglect or stupidity. The men of 1905 had carefully considered the future and did not like what they saw; faced with a life-and-death gamble they played and won. The issues at stake were such that the continued neglect of the Central Docks was not only defensible, it was the only defensible course.

By the late 1870s the Mersey Docks and Harbour Board had become a highly ineffective body which combined poor planning and management with a high degree of complacency. In the 1880s the situation deteriorated even further, and it is not until 1890 that the Board showed signs of recognizing that it had a problem, which was the obvious prerequisite of any action to solve it. By 1905, a growing

'Excuse me, your shoe-string is showing.' Beneath its smart exterior, Riverside Station concealed various improvisations on left-overs from previous buildings, including this 1843 column from the first secure transit sheds

(Colin Pitcher)

determination to accept the inherited difficulties and set the port back on its feet had led to some wise decisions. At the same time, the standard of engineering work, which accounted for a large part of the Board's expenditure and had a crucial effect on the attractiveness of the service they could offer, reached a trough in the 1880s and improved at an accelerating rate as A.G. Lyster emerged from the shadow of his father from 1891 onwards. The changes happened in time to save the port from the collapse which at times seemed a distinct possibility, but too late for the Central Docks to benefit from anything beyond piecemeal improvements.

APPENDIX 1

The Claim of Eckersley, Godfrey and Liddlelow Against the Board

The circumstances of this claim are briefly recounted in Chapter Two, and may be summarized here as based on allegations that the work of the Engineer's Department was so badly carried out as to cause serious loss to the contractor. A High Court writ was issued on 27 October 1893, making a total claim of £40,057 8s 2d. In its printed form, the Statement of Claim alone ran to thirteen pages of foolscap and is, therefore, overlong to reproduce complete, but the three following extracts have been selected as fairly typical.

Claim 20 presents a detailed picture of the extent of the plant and manpower deployed on what was, at that date, a medium sized rather than a large improvement to the dock system. Perhaps more interesting, in view of the obscurity of the Board's own figures as to what things actually cost, it gives exact costings on every item claimed, resulting in an unusually clear picture of what was actually happening on the ground when hundreds of thousands of cubic yards of spoil were being moved around.

Claim 30 is an indication of the indirect costs of a serious failure (which caused the complete inundation of the site), while the summary of Claim 46 is a horrifying indication of the way in which comparatively minor indecision on the part of the Board's staff caused site costs to rise.

The complete claim and details of its out-of-court settlement may be found in WUP 17/1.

Appendix 1

Claim 20 . . . . *£68 1 10*

To loss and injury sustained owing to the tides flowing through the sewers, flooding the works and stopping all operations for 2½ hours on three consecutive days.

1891 – 8, 9, and 10 April

3½ days,	Locomotive	46s 0d	£8	1	0
1½ "	Steam Navvy	46s 0d	3	9	0
30 hours,	Steam Crane	3s 6d	5	5	0
120 days,	Wagon	2s 0d	12	0	0
3½ "	Engine Driver	7s 6d	1	6	3
3½ "	Labourer – Roperunner	6s 0d	1	1	0
3½ "	do. – Flagman	6s 0d	1	1	0
3½ "	do. – Cleaners	6s 0d	1	1	0
1½ "	Steam Navvy Driver	7s 6d	0	11	3
1½ "	do. Wheelman	6s 0d	0	9	0
1½ "	do. Fireman	6s 0d	0	9	0
2¼ "	Ganger at Steam Navvy and Tip	9s 7d	1	1	7
1½ "	do. at Crane	11s 6d	0	17	3
ON ROADS:					
9¾ days	Labourer	6s 0d	2	18	6
IN TRENCHES:					
50 days,	Labourer	6s 0d	15	0	0
9¾ "	Boys	2s10½d	1	8	0
4½ "	Timbermen	8s 0d	1	16	0
13¼ "	Labourer	6s 0d	3	19	6
AT TIP:					
13¾ days,	Labourer	6s 0d	4	2	6
3¾ "	Horse and Driver	12s 0d	2	5	0
			£68	1	10

Claim 30 . . . . *£1,282 4 0*

To injury sustained and depreciation of value of plant and materials by the water breaking through from the Canada Dock, also for general expenses and loss from 15 February to 31 March, namely, 29 days, exclusive of Sunday, at £30 per day: £1,170 0 0

The charge of £30 per day is made up as follows:

Value of plant on ground	£22,583 0 8
Less value of plant hired by Board and that buried in Dock	7,220 0 0
	£15,363 0 8

Value of plant depreciated by stoppage at 20% per annum of 300 days, per day	£10 4 10
Interest on capital at 10% per annum, per day . . .	5 17 1
Interest on retentions, £5,309 17s 4d, at 10% per annum, per day	1 15 5
Proportion of London Office Expenses	7 0 0
Liverpool Office Expenses	5 0 0
	£29 17 4

Say per day £30.

Depreciation in value of plant and materials buried in and recovered from bottom of Dock, viz.:	
£2,200 for 39 days at 20% per annum	57 4 0
Special repairs over and above amount of depreciation	55 0 0
	£1,282 4 0

APPENDIX 1

Claim 46 . . . . *£12,212 18 0*

To loss and injury sustained in excavating the body of the Dock owing to hindrances and delays and frequent laying, taking up and relaying temporary roads for wagons, moving and removing from time to time the steam navvies, also from increased engine power necessary to draw trucks up steeper inclines, all such matters being contrary to the Contract for the work, consequent upon the retention by the Board of portions of the site for sundry purposes, whereby a daily diminution of output of excavation was the result, and the work done was done at an increased cost, a close approximation of the value of such increased cost and of the loss upon increased plant, extended time of working and establishment charges is estimated to be 6d per cubic yard upon the 490,732 yards excavated other than in trenches.

490,732 yards cube	Excavation	
2,216 " "	Deduct for pitcher paving otherwise charged for	
488,516 " "	Excavation 0s 6d	
		£12,212 18 0

APPENDIX 2

The Dock Acts

The Acts of Parliament relating to the Liverpool Dock Estate could form the subject of a substantial book in their own right. Copies of Acts and Bills, together with their Committee Proceedings, proofs of evidence etc. occur in the MDHB collection in four main places: in the Legal Files, in the minutes of the Parliamentary Committee, in the Printed Works sequence and in the long sequence of Worked up Papers No. 60. The Plans collection contains a substantial number of drawings which became or were intended to become deposited plans.

The short list that follows gives brief particulars of those Acts which have particular relevance to the Central Docks 1799–1905.

1799 Various powers granted: this Act authorized Princes Dock, but no action resulted.

1811 Renewed powers to build Princes Dock. Authorized boundary walls for first time, established Audit Commission, Charitable Fund and dock police, borrowing powers for £600,000. Allowed charges to be made on tonnage of vessel and cargo, instead of vessel only, as previously.

1813 Authorized Government loan for the continuation of works at Princes Dock.

1819 Granted powers to build residences on dock estate (as at Princes and Salisbury entrances).

1825 Constitutional changes to Dock Committee, restriction of role of Audit Commissioners, powers to build Clarence, Waterloo and Victoria Docks.

A second act of the same year granted further borrowing powers.

1828 Further borrowing powers.

1830 Further borrowing powers. Both these acts related mainly to land purchase costs.

1841 Best known for authorizing Albert Dock, but also authorized the secure transit sheds at West Princes Dock.

1844 Powers to build new 'North Docks': Salisbury, Collingwood, Stanley, Nelson, Bramley-Moore, Wellington.

1848 Authorized Sandon and Huskisson Docks.

1851 Altered the Constitution of the Dock Committee.

1855 Enabled Canada Dock and improvements at Waterloo (not completed until 1868).

1857 Incorporated the Birkenhead Docks as part of the Port of Liverpool, and established MDHB.

1858 MDHB Consolidation Act rationalized powers under existing Acts.

1871 Enabled the closure of Georges Dock Basin and remodelling of Pier Head.

1873 Enabled huge extensions at both north and south ends of the estate: £4.1 million.

1876 Enabled second thoughts on Canada entrance.

1891 To alter and improve the alterations and improvements at the north end under the 1873 Act.

1898 To alter and improve Sandon Dock, also Kings, Queens and Brunswick.

APPENDIX 3

The Dock Board's Financial Problems at the End of Last Century

(extracted and calculated from the published annual accounts)

	1870	1880	1890	1900
Water acreage of docks open to traffic	236.01	317.78	362.81	366.19
Total Dues(Dock Dues, Town Dues, Tonnage Dues & Anchorage Dues) received	£743,910	£1,022,783	£1,069,822	£1,092,809
Total Debt (Bonds, Annuities, Promissory Notes)	£14.4m	£15.9m	£17.1m	£23.9m
Total Interest	£642,509	£678,948	£683,756	£679,356
Revenue cost of Engineer's Dept[1]	£97,758	£162,715	£191,082	£211,836
'General Charges' Secretary's Dept, Treasurer's, Chief Account's etc.	£31,864	£48,648	£71,233	£76,004
Dues income as % of total debt	5.1%	6.4%	6.2%	4.5%
Interest as % of dues income	86%	66%	63%	62%
Engineering cost as % of dues income[2]	13.15%	15.92%	17.88%	19.38%
General charges as % of dues income[2]	4.2%	4.7%	6.6%	6.9%
Engineering cost/acre	£414	£512	£526	£578
General charges/acre	£135	£153	£196	£207

APPENDIX 3

Notes

1 Excluding improvement work charged to capital budgets.
2 Excluding all departments (e.g. harbourmaster's) which were active in the Board's core services to customers. The figure should have *reduced*, since the number of ships was declining as their average size rose, which meant that there were fewer individual transactions.

Deductions

1 The fact that debt rose consistently while the affordability of its interest cost also rose indicates that the Board was moderately successful in the rolling refinancing of its Bond Debt. The Bond Debt became a problem when rolling refinancing became difficult.
2 The bureaucratic accretion recounted in Chapter Six is reflected in the constant rise of overheads as a proportion of revenue and in relation to the area served.
3 The stagnant revenues from 1880 onwards did not really justify either continued major capital expenditure or the cut in tonnage rates made in 1885.

APPENDIX 4

Summary of Liverpool Docks, from Mersey Docks and Harbour Board Pocket Yearbook 1920

THE DOCKS AT LIVERPOOL AND BIRKENHEAD.

DATES OF OPENING AND AREAS.

OPENED.		LIVERPOOL.			AREA.	
					Acres.	Yards.
1715...	31st August	The Old Dock			3	1890
1753...		Salthouse Dock			4	3665
1771...		George's Dock			4	4455
1788...	3rd Oct. ...	King's Dock			7	3896
1796...	17th April...	Queen's Dock			6	2526
1816...	28th Oct. ...	Enlargement of Queen's Dock	4	575		
		Union Dock	2	3505	6	4080
1821...	19th July ...	Prince's Dock			11	3889
1825...	30th April...	Enlargement of George's Dock			0	2978
		Area of Docks opened between 1715 *and* 1825...			46	3179
1826...	31st August	The Old Dock closed ... ... *deduct*			3	1890
					43	1289
1829...	12th Dec. ...	Canning Dock (previously called The Dry Dock)...			3	4575
1830...	6th Sept....	Clarence Dock...	6	273		
		Clarence Half-Tide Dock	3	4500		
		Clarence Graving Dock Basin	0	4072	10	4005
1832...	14th April...	Brunswick Dock	12	2744		
		Brunswick Half-Tide Dock	1	3388	14	1292
1834...	6th Sept....	Waterloo Dock			6	1153
1836...	30th July ...	Victoria Dock...	5	4159		
		Trafalgar Dock	6	2643	12	1962
1840...		Coburg Dock (altered from Brunswick Basin) ...			4	2198
1842...	9th May ...	Enlargement of Canning Dock	0	641		
		Toxteth Dock	1	469		
			1	1110		
	October ...	Salthouse Dock (reduced in area) ...	0	172	1	938
1844...		Canning Half-Tide Dock (previously called Old Dock Gut)	2	2688		
		Harrington Dock purchased	0	3740	3	1588
1845...	6th Feb. ...	Albert Dock			7	3542
1848...	4th August	Salisbury Dock	3	2146		
		Collingwood Dock...	5	244		
		Stanley Dock	7	120		
		Nelson Dock	7	4786		
		Bramley-Moore Dock	9	3106		
		Enlargement of Clarence Graving Dock Basin	0	1824		
			33	2546		
		Continued			107	3182

THE DOCKS AT LIVERPOOL AND BIRKENHEAD—CONTINUED.

OPENED.		LIVERPOOL.			AREA.	
					Acres.	Yards.
		Continued			107	3182
		Victoria Dock—River Entrance closed	33	2546		
		in 1846 ... ... *deduct*	0	600	33	1946
1850...		Wellington Dock	7	4120		
		Wellington Half-Tide Dock	3	813	11	93
1851...	May	Sandon Dock	10	100		
		Huskisson East Lock	0	4682		
		Huskisson West Lock	0	3650	11	3592
		Manchester Dock purchased			1	910
1852...	1st April...	Huskisson Dock			14	3451
1853...		Enlargement of Clarence Half-Tide Dock			0	2134
1855...	27th Jan. ...	Enlargement of Salthouse Dock ...	1	3366		
	9th May ...	Wapping Dock	5	499		
		Wapping Basin	1	3151	8	2176
1856...	10th May ...	Queen's Half-Tide Dock	3	3542		
	4th August	Queen's Dock re-opened, after deepening and walls re-built ... *deduct*	0	1537	3	2005
1858...	27th Feb. ...	Coburg and Union Docks united ...	0	4003		
		Passage to Brunswick Dock enlarged	0	266		
1858...	9th August	Canada Dock	17	4043		
		Canada Lock	1	3479		
		Lightbody Street Basin	0	920	20	3031
1861...	29th June...	Huskisson Branch Dock, No. 2			7	592
1862...	17th Feb. ...	Brocklebank Dock (name changed from Canada Half-Tide Dock, May 23, 1879)	3	4380		
		North Carriers' Dock	2	3423		
		South do. do.	1	4515	8	2638
1866...	16th March	Herculaneum Dock (name changed from Herculaneum Half-Tide Dock, 8th Oct., 1885)			3	3000
		Area of Docks opened between 1715 *and* 1866 ...			231	4550
1868...	4th July ...	Prince's Half-Tide Dock	4	3250		
		East Waterloo Dock...	2	3375		
		West Waterloo Dock	3	2146		
		Deduct—	10	3931		
		Old Waterloo Dock 5 3056				
		Do. Lock 0 2937				
		Part of North Lock, Prince's Dock 0 2399	6	3552	4	379
1871...	9th August	Brocklebank Dock enlargement			7	1470
1872...	30th July ...	Huskisson Branch Dock, No. 3			8	780
	30th July ...	River Craft Dock and Lock purchased by the Board from the Corporation, and transferred 1st July, 1876			0	4102
		Continued			252	1601

THE DOCKS AT LIVERPOOL AND BIRKENHEAD—CONTINUED.

OPENED.		LIVERPOOL.			AREA.	
					Acres.	Yards.
		Continued...			252	1601
1878...	26th August	Brunswick Branch Dock	1	2129		
		Less Railway Co.'s portion	0	2334	0	4635
1879...	23rd May ...	Langton Dock	18	589		
		Langton Branch Dock	2	4549		
		Deduct—	21	298		
		Harrington Dock, absorbed by new works, under Act 1873	0	3740	20	1398
1880...	3rd Dec. ...	Alexandra Dock	17	4055		
		Do. Branch Dock, No. 3	7	3420		
		Do. do. „ 2	9	2657		
		Do. do. „ 1	9	573	44	1025
1881...	6th May ...	Herculaneum Dock, enlargement ..	3	4421		
		Herculaneum Branch Dock	2	853	6	434
	8th Sept....	Langton West Lock (238 feet long) ...	0	1719		
		Do. East Lock (119 „ „) ...	0	860	0	2579
1883...	23rd July ...	Harrington Dock (name changed from Dock, North of Herculaneum Half-tide Dock, 8th Oct., 1885)	9	256		
		Do. Lock (131 feet long)	0	320	9	576
1884...	17th Jan. ...	Hornby Dock	16	3769		
		Do. Branch Dock	0	3354		
		Deduct—	17	2283		
		Toxteth Dock, absorbed in 1885 by new works under Act 1873	1	469	16	1814
1888...	8th May ...	Toxteth Dock (made under Act of 1873)	11	1075		
		Do. Lock (177 feet long)	0	1013	11	2088
1889...	2nd Dec....	Union Dock	1	1941		
		Brunswick Dock (additional area) ...	0	354	1	2295
					362	3925
1895...		Certain slight alterations at Canada Lock reduce the area by			0	1461
					362	2464
1896...		Enlargement of Canada Dock	6	1710		
	19th May ...	Canada Branch Dock No. 1	7	2313	13	4023
		Continued...			376	1647

THE DOCKS AT LIVERPOOL AND BIRKENHEAD—CONTINUED.

OPENED.		LIVERPOOL.			AREA.	
					Acres.	Yards.
		Continued...			376	1647
1896...		Certain alterations at North end of Huskisson Dk. and Huskisson East Lock reduce the area by			5	3293
		Deduct—			370	3194
1897...		Huskisson West Lock, absorbed by Works under Act, 1891	0	3650		
		Stanley Dock, South portion filled in for Tobacco Warehouses	3	1617	4	427
					366	2767
		Widening of Hornby Passage			0	911
1900...	28th April..	Duke's Dock purchased	2	1336		
	July...	Trafalgar-Victoria Passage widening	0	1568		
	Sept...	Huskisson Dk., extension southwdly.	2	4273		
	Nov....	Brunswick Dock, alteration of North and West Passages...	0	169	5	2506
		Deduct—			372	1344
	Oct ...	Brunswick Half-Tide Dock, alterations East Quay	0	1989		
	Nov....	Coburg Dock, alterations North Quay and South Passage...	0	1709		
1900...	1st Dec....	George's Dock and part of Passage closed	5	1560	6	418
					366	926
1901...	July...	Sandon Half-Tide Dock	14	466		
	Oct. ...	Queen's Dock widening	0	1560		
	Oct. ...	Queen's Branch Dock, No. 1	4	4384	19	1570
					385	2496
		Deduct—				
		Wellington Half-Tide Dock	3	813		
		River Craft Dock and Lock	0	4102	4	75
					381	2421
1902...	May...	Huskisson Branch Dock, No 1...			9	1125
		Deduct—			390	3546
		Brunswick Branch Dock (*less* Railway Co.'s portion) } absorbed by New Works }			0	4635
					389	3751
	Sept...	Sandon Half-Tide Dock—				
		North Lock (130 feet long)	0	1155		
		Middle ,, (165 ,, ,,)	0	733		
		South ,, (130 ,, ,,)	0	1444	0	3332
					390	2243
1903...	Aug....	Canada Branch Dock, No. 2			6	2560
		Continued...			396	4803

THE DOCKS AT LIVERPOOL AND BIRKENHEAD—CONTINUED.

OPENED.		LIVERPOOL.			AREA.	
					Acres.	Yards.
		Continued			396	4803
1903...	Aug....	Brunswick North Lock (240 feet long)	0	2133		
		,, South ,, (350 ,, ,,)	0	3889	1	1182
		Deduct—			398	1145
		South Carriers' Dock			1	4515
					396	1470
1905...	July ...	Queen's Branch Dock No. 2			5	140
		Deduct—			401	1610
		Queen's Half-Tide Dock	3	3542		
		Prince's Dock (portion)	1	609	4	4151
					396	2299
1906...	Jan. ...	King's Dock No. 1	4	3263		
	Sep. ...	Do. No. 2	4	2055		
	Nov....	Canada Branch Dock No. 3	7	1625		
		Langton Dock (alterations)	0	728		
		Brocklebank Dock (alterations)... ...	0	2911		
		Canada Dock (alterations)	0	496		

GLOSSARY

Annealing Wrought iron lifting tackle gradually work-hardens with use, becoming brittle – and dangerous. The annealing process, in which the tackle is heated in an oven, maintained at high temperature for some hours and then cooled slowly, restores the original properties of the iron.

Archimedean Screw Pump A pump which moves fluids (or quasi-fluids like bulk grain) by the rotation of a helical rotor within a casing. Familiar as the means of moving meat into the cutters of the ordinary domestic mincing machine.

Chronometer A spring-driven mechanical clock of sufficient accuracy to allow timings taken from it to be used to calculate the position of a ship.

Economizer A device for pre-heating the feedwater for a steam boiler using waste heat either from the flues or from exhaust steam. Depending on the efficiency of the rest of the system, they saved about 5–10 per cent on fuel consumption.

Fairlead A deck fixture on a ship which fulfils the same purpose as an idler roller.

Forecastle Originally, the elevated fighting deck at the front of a medieval warship. The term continues in use to mean the deck at the sharp end and the accommodation below it. Pronounced fo'csle.

Greenheart A tropical hardwood, usually imported from Central America. One of the few woods dense enough to sink in water, it is obtainable in huge baulks. Other properties are exceptional weather resistance and almost complete immunity from attack by boring insects, worms etc.

Hogshead (dry) A package (like a sack or bale) chiefly used in the North American tobacco trade. Contents could vary between 600 and 1800 lb, depending on the kind of leaf and the density of packing.

Idler Roller (1) An additional roller added to those which actually carry a transit band, whose axis may be moved to keep the band at a constant tension. An analogous device tensions the camshaft drive belts of most modern cars.

Idler Rollers (2) Small bobbin-shaped rollers mounted on quaysides, especially around passages or entrances to change the direction of pull exerted by a rope from a winch or capstan when warping an unpowered vessel.

Sidereal (*time*) Throughout the period covered by this book, the most accurate way of determining time was by measuring the apparent movement of a star (Latin – *sidus*, a star).

Staithe A high-level jetty, usually of wooden construction, built to carry road or rail vehicles to the side of deep water to allow tipping of minerals, usually coal, directly into a ship's hold. There is a spectacular, preserved example on the Tyne.

Stevedore A skilled dock worker whose job is the loading of cargo. The porters get the goods to the ship's side, thereafter the stevedores take over. The corresponding workers discharging a ship are *lumpers*.

Water-hammer Violent vibrations in a pipe carrying water under pressure. Often encountered in domestic plumbing owing to worn taps or ballcocks. Its effects at the working pressures of hydraulic power stations were more unpleasant.

ARCHIVAL SOURCES

1 *The Mersey Docks and Harbour Board Collection*

This enormous collection (over 150 tons of paper) is mostly housed in the Maritime Record Centre of Merseyside Maritime Museum, Albert Dock, Liverpool. Virtually all the unpublished source material used in this book comes from that collection, and the following is a summary of the main documents used.

1/1 Minutes

Minutes of the Dock Committee. Ref. 1/1 - 1/18, 1793–1857.
Minutes of the Sub-committee of Works. Ref. 7/1 - 7/4, 1840–57.
Minutes of the Commissioners appointed by Act of Parliament to inspect, audit and adjust the accounts of the Trustees of the Liverpool Docks. Ref. 19/4. 1822–53.
Minutes of the Mersey Docks & Harbour Board. Ref. 9/1–9/27. 1858–1905.
Minutes of the Docks & Quays Committee (of MDHB). Ref. 12/1–12/21, 1858–1905.
Minutes of the Traffic Committee. Ref. 15/1a–15/20, 1862–1904.
Minutes of the Warehouse Committee. Ref. 16/1–16/17, 1858–1904.
Minutes of the Works Committee. Ref. 17/1–17/20, 1858–1906.
Discussions at the Board (verbatim). Ref. 1–247, 1867–1905.

Indexed in handlist

All the above, except Discussions at the Board, are indexed either at the back of the volume or in a companion volume.

1/2 Legal Files

File A/1: Liverpool Dock Bills 1840–51, with various earlier papers appended.
File A/7: Liverpool Docks Bill 1855, with various earlier items appended.
Files E6 & E7: Rex versus John Joseph Lynch and John Rous: re wages frauds in Engineer's Dept.
File H25: re dock police officers.
File H80: Working of the Trade of the Port: Appointment of General Manager.

1/3 Worked up Papers, bound
No. 9, vol. 1. Claims upon the Board 1863–95.
No. 17, vol. 1. Dock Improvements 1889–96.
No. 29, vol. 1. Cattle Trade Accommodation (general) 1865–81.
No. 34, vol. 1 & 2. High Level Coal Railway, 1850–1925.
No. 36, vol. 1. Huts, Cocoa vans etc., 1862–83.
No. 55, vol. 1. New works at the north end, 1873–86.
No. 59, vols 1 & 2. Overhead Railway, 1853–90.
No. 60/1904. Parliamentary Session, 1904.
No. 83, vol 1. Transit Sheds, 1854–1900.
No. 93, vol. 1. New Dock Offices, 1898–1913.
No. 95, vol. 1. Docking, Berthing and Discharging of Vessels, 1844–1914.
No. 100, vol. 1. Coal Contracts, 1865–1912.
No. 148, vol. 1. Charitable Fund, 1863–1937.
No. 152, vol. 1. Cold Storage Accommodation, 1884–1935.
No. 158, vol. 1. *Galatea*, Board's Steamer, 1894–1948.

1/4 Worked up Papers, unbound
C 127. Coal Returns, High Level Railway.
E 13. As to working Enclosed Docks as Open Docks.
I8b. Irregularities, Engineer's Department. Also various other 'Irregularities' papers listed under 'I'.
O2a. Offices &c on the Docks Quays – Huts and Cocoa vans: Newspaper criticisms.
V19. Vessels anchoring in the track of ferry boats.
Berth papers: are listed in UWUP sequence under the name of the company (whether owner or manager) to whom the berth was appropriated.

1/5 Staff & Wages Documents
vol. SW 1/2, begun 1850 and vol. SW 1/16.

1/6 Printed Annual Accounts
Fin 1/2 – 1/6, 1858–1910.

1/7 Other MDHB material
Engineer's Department Total Cost of Works Ledgers 1868–1905. (in store)
Report of the Dock Surveyor/Engineer/Engineer-in-Chief.
Microfiche copies, 1836–1905.
Old Agreement Book. Microfiche Copy. 1811–71.
Miscellaneous File 17/3/c.

2 *Material in Liverpool Record Office*
The Gregson Papers. Ref. 920 GRE. Several items relating to the docks at the turn of the nineteenth century.
The Cotton Exchange Cuttings Book.
Printed account of the proceedings of the Special Committee on Dock Accommodation, 1870.
Reports of the Astronomer (catalogued under Bidston Observatory).
Microfilm copies of local newspapers.

NOTES

Abbreviations Used in the Notes

1 Locations

Liv. RO Liverpool Record Office.

Primary material cited with no location given is in the Maritime Record Centre, Merseyside Maritime Museum (MRC).

2 Sources

MDHB Mersey Docks and Harbour Board.

DCM Dock Committee Minutes. Predecessor of the above, pre-1858.

SCW Minutes of the Sub Committee of Works (of the Dock Committee).

Board Minutes of meetings of MDHB.

Discussions at Board Verbatim minutes on selected topics.

D&Q The Docks and Quays Committee of MDHB.

Works The Works Committee of MDHB.

Traffic The Traffic Committee of MDHB.

(Other committees' minutes are only infrequently cited, e.g. Warehouse Committee.)

Eng. Rep. Engineer's Report. This document, produced annually from 1836 on, has several changes in its title over the years, which have been disregarded for purposes of citation.

TCW The Engineer's Department's ledger of Total Cost of Works.

WUP A subject file compiled for the use of the Board from a variety of sources.

UWUP A similar file but not bound in a volume. UWUPs have a separate numbering system.

Agreements Book A book inaugurated after the Audit Commission was established in 1811 in which were to be recorded all contracts entered into for goods or services. In fact by no means all contracts were entered.

BPP British Parliamentary Papers. In each of the reports cited, the originals have been repaginated, so to avoid confusion, the citation has been made by Question Number.

3 Journals

Min. Proc. ICE Minutes of the Proceedings of the Institution of Civil Engineers.
Proc. IME Proceedings of the Institution of Mechanical Engineers.
TLES Transactions of the Liverpool Engineering Society.
THSLC Transactions of the Historic Society of Lancashire and Cheshire.
Mercury The *Liverpool Mercury*.
Jnl Comm. The *Journal of Commerce*.

4 Frequently Cited Published Works

Gore's Annals Originally published as an Appendix to Gore's *Liverpool Directory*, but more conveniently found in reprint form as F. Spiegl (ed.) *An Everyday History of Liverpool*, 2 vols, Liverpool, UD.
Picton J.A. Picton, *Memorials of Liverpool*, 2 vols, 3rd edn (Liverpool, 1903).
Mountfield S.B. Mountfield, *Western Gateway* (Liverpool, 1965).
Hyde F.E. Hyde, *Liverpool and The Mersey* (Newton Abbot, 1971).

Chapter One The Early Development of the Port

1 E.H. Rideout, 'The Development of the Liverpool Warehousing System', *THSLC*, vol. 82 (1930), pp. 5–6.
2 D. Richardson, 'Profits in the Liverpool Slave Trade: the Accounts of William Davenport, 1757–84', R. Anstey and P.E.H. Hair (eds), *Liverpool, the African Slave Trade and Abolition*, HSLC Occasional Series, vol. 2 (1976), p. 77.
3 These and other triumphs of Liverpool Privateers are reported in *Gore's Annals*.
4 *BPP* 1835 (116) XXVI.1.
5 For other aspects of their activities see: A.E. Jarvis, 'The Interests and Ethics of John Foster, Liverpool Dock Surveyor', *THSLC* forthcoming. H.Booth, *Henry Booth*, Ilfracombe, (1980). B. Keith-Lucas, *The Unreformed Local Government System* (1980).
6 The account which follows is based on the appendices to *BPP* 1856 (332) XII.1, which include a massive recital of all the documentation establishing Liverpool Corporation's title to Town Dues.
7 The passage which follows is counter-factual, with the doubts that such an approach entails, but is based on the provisions of the 1785 Improvement Act.
8 Hanging in chains was admittedly uncommon by this date. Indeed it may be that John Smith, who was sufficiently ill-advised to be convicted of burgling the Custom House, whose mortal remains were displayed at Beacon's Gutter from August 1766 to April 1769, was the last. The legal provision continued to exist until 1834, the same year in which the pillory was abolished. Public whipping of women was abolished in 1817.
9 T.C. Barker and J.R. Harris, *A Merseyside Town in the Industrial Revolution* (Liverpool, 1954), pp. 226–31.
10 Jarvis *op. cit.* and 'Harold Littledale, the Man with a Mission', H.M. Hignett (ed.), *A Second Merseyside Maritime History*, Liverpool Nautical Research Society Occasional Series (Liverpool, 1991), pp. 5–16. See also Chapter Two below.

11 Pre-1939 MDHB Pocket Yearbooks contain a useful tabulation of docks, giving dates of construction, entrance sizes and water areas, reproduced as Appendix 4.
12 See Chapter Two below.
13 Mountfield could also have remarked that a House of Commons Select Committee on Local Charges on Shipping in Ports of the United Kingdom sat in the smoke and gloom of Westminster. It asked 5,163 questions and published a report of over 700 pages which relates almost entirely to Liverpool. That is the true origin of the establishment of MDHB. *BPP* 1856 (332) XII.1.

Chapter Two Fingers in the Till

Ideas of Honesty

1 *Gore's Annals* include regular references to executions for theft.
2 Superintendent Dowling's statement was examined by a Special Sub-Committee of the Dock Committee, 10–17 August 1836. Its papers survive in Legal File H25/1.
3 See Legal Files E6 and E7, and below, section 3.

Weighed in the Balance and Found Wanting

4 For a succinct explanation of unreformed borough administration see D. Fraser, *Power and Authority in the Victorian City* (Oxford, 1979), Chapter One. For a specific port-based argument, see G. Bush, *Bristol and its Municipal Government, 1820–1851* (Bristol Record Society, 1976), which deals with both unreformed and reformed local government.
5 The change is indicated by the inauguration of the new sequence of minutes. MDHB 1/1–18.
6 DCM 7 December 1799.
7 Audit Commission minutes survive unbroken from 25 June 1822 to 1853. MDHB 19/4.
8 For example, on 2 July 1818, John Smith contracted to remove a heap of rubbish at 6d per cubic yard.
9 For example in DCM 4 May 1810.
10 Enquiries began along these lines on 8 October 1822. Audit 19/4, p. 3.
11 ibid. pp. 20–1. For brickworks see p. 35.
12 ibid. pp. 4–5.
13 The iron issue was argued out at great length, pp. 43–53.
14 It is categorically stated that 'No articles are provided by public contract' pp. 18–19.
15 Agreements Book 21 October 1823, p. 287.
16 An Abstract of Title shows the three men as co-owners of the Birkenhead Ferry and Hotel. Liv. RO, ref. 920 GRE 3/9.
17 One a little later does. Grindrod contracted for masonry work at seven shillings per cubic yard, workmanship only, for the extension to the river wall northwards. Agreements Book 8/1/24, p. 287.
18 This method was not invariably successful. See below.

19 Not all chief engineers would admit this: in the Evidence for the 1825 Bill for the Liverpool and Manchester Railway, George Stephenson attempted to lay the blame for the fundamental surveying errors on very junior assistants, one of whom subsequently committed suicide.
20 R.H.G. Thomas, *The Liverpool and Manchester Railway*, (Newton Abbot, 1980), p. 37.
21 The report survives in the *Telford Papers* at the Institution of Civil Engineers, ref. T/LM13. The key points are summarized in Thomas *op. cit.* pp. 50–3. See also A. Penfold, 'Management Organisation on the Caledonian Canal', *Thomas Telford, Engineer*, (1980).
22 J.H.M. Banckes and J.R. Harris, 'The First Lancashire Locomotive', *Journal of Transport History*, vol. 5 (1961–2), p. 146.
23 At a cost of £1125 3s 0d. DCM 9 June 1816.
24 DCM 24 November 1813.
25 W.N. Slatcher, 'The Barnsley Canal: its first twenty years', *Transport History*, vol. 1 (1968), pp. 55–6. S.R. Broadbridge, 'John Pinkerton and the Birmingham Canals', *Transport History*, vol. 4 (1971), pp. 33–49.
26 DCM 10 June 1819 and 19 January 1819 respectively.
27 DCM 10 May 1819.
28 DCM 15 July 1819 and 6 September 1819.
29 DCM 15 July and 17 February 1819 respectively.
30 The surveyor was to provide a furnace to burn what remained after this process. DCM 26 January 1837.
31 DCM 15 July 1819.

Revelations of a Victorian Whistleblower

32 The campaign against Town Dues (see Chapter One above) was the main manifestation of this; such things as the revelation of a near 1000 per cent overspend on St George's Hall did little to pacify the opposition.
33 The old passages are 45–50 ft. TSMV Overchurch is 40 ft 8 in wide excluding fenders.
34 Most of the original drawings for this work survive in MRC. Brief details are given in Eng. Rep. 1865–9.
35 Minute of the Common Council transcribed into DCM 2 June 1824.
36 Report of the meeting of the Works Committee, *Liverpool Daily Post*, 15 June 1877.
37 Board, 31 January 1878.
38 Works, 2 November 1883.
39 *Liverpool Mercury* 15 May 1885.
40 G.F. Lyster, *The History of the Birkenhead Great Low Water Basin* (Liverpool, 1864), is an apologia for this.
41 Report by William Cubitt to the Dock Committee 4 November 1847. Cubitt suggested moving the stage bodily downstream: Lyster extended it upstream and wondered why it grounded at low-water springs.
42 Even after essential alterations to improve fire protection (Works, 10 August 1875) the insurance premiums on Lyster's warehouses in Liverpool were at 6s 0d per cent. See also Chapter Seven, Note 24.

43 Quoted in a letter from Harold Littledale to the Editor, *Liverpool Daily Courier*, 17 April 1883.
44 There is a particularly scornful comment in the Editorial, *Liverpool Daily Post*, 26 February 1886.
45 The ongoing problems of the Canada entrance can be followed in WUP 17/1.
46 Works, 16 August 1895.
47 Writ in Queen's Bench, 27 October 1893. Copied in WUP 17/1. Appendix 1 contains transcribed extracts from the claim.
48 Works, 6 November 1885.
49 The root cause was the failure to admit that twenty years and seven digits sterling had been spent trying to improve an entrance which would never work.
50 Ironically, several of the witnesses examined by the 1902 Royal Commission to examine the Port of London held up Liverpool as a model of efficiency and economy for London to emulate. *BPP* 1902 (1151) XLIII.222. See also Chapter Nine, below.
51 The summary of the Lynch case which follows is based on the contents of Legal Files E6 and 7. Lynch's MS confession, written and signed while on remand in Walton Gaol is the most important single item.
52 Presumably a misspelling of 'Pommery' the Champagne shipper. A moderate vintage champagne at that time cost about 7s–8s per bottle. If 13s is correct it must represent an old-landed champagne of *c.*1860!

The Landscape of Dishonesty

53 For these and other bureaucratic excesses, see E. Hoon, *The English Customs Service 1696–1786* (New York, 1938), pp. 25–37.
54 The colourful activities of Sir Thomas Johnson have a little bibliography all their own. See for example C.N. Parkinson, *The Rise of the Port of Liverpool* (Liverpool, 1952), pp. 72–83.
55 According to *Gore's Annals* it was not until 1780 that the docks even had chains around them to help prevent people blundering into them in the dark.
56 MDHB Miscellaneous file 17/3/c contains a leisurely correspondence between HM Customs and John Foster, extending from 1804–14.
57 *Gore's Annals* 1802.
58 T. Troughton, *The History of Liverpool* (Liverpool, 1810), p. 275.
59 From a printed account of a 'Numerous Meeting of the Owners of Land and Warehouses' 28 March 1838. See also letters from 'Justitia' to the Editor, *Liverpool Albion*, 24 March and 31 March 1838.
60 DCM 4 Feb 1805.
61 Legal File H25 includes his evidence as well as the enquiry into his giving it.
62 The Liverpool Customs Collector received a letter from his superiors demanding to know the height and thickness of the wall, 17 April 1813. MDHB Miscellaneous 17/3/c.
63 DCM 25 January 1822.
64 They were not necessarily used for bonded goods, especially during the Irish potato season. For problems with rum, see WUP 83/1, minute of 14 July 1880 *et seq.*

Chapter Three 1848 – *Annus Mirabilis*

1 Jessop's report is transcribed in DCM 1 May 1800.
2 On the basis of Rennie's report, presented to the Dock Committee 14 August 1809.
3 Agreements Book, 9 August 1825, p. 336.
4 At Runcorn, for example, the entrance lock was the size of a Mersey flat.
5 DCM 26 October 1830. Any other vessels entering incurred a fine of £5.
6 Eng. Rep. 1847.
7 The original design was for a tower 150 ft high at a cost of £4,500. The tower as it stands now is basically the same design shorn of its turret – and of some £2,350. The original design was by 'Mr Hardwick' of Albert Dock and Euston Arch fame. SCW 5 September 1846.
8 These and other complaints were given in Evidence for the 1844 Dock Act. Legal File A1/1.
9 WUP 34/1 contains Hartley's report presented 7 November 1850, together with extracts from minutes of meeting leading to and proceeding from the production of the report.
10 Eng. Rep. 1850.
11 The 1841 figures given in evidence for 1844 Dock Act, earlier figures from Hyde Appendix 1.
12 The sorry tale of the beginnings of Birkenhead Docks is disentangled in K. McCarron, *The Fall and Rise of Birkenhead Docks*, Merseyside Port Folios (forthcoming).
13 Eng. Rep. 1844–8.
14 For accounts of the life and work of navvies see: Terry Coleman, *The Railway Navvies* (Harmondsworth, 1968), and Dick Sullivan, *Navvyman* (1983).
15 *BPP* 1846 (530) XIII. 425, questions 3042 *et seq.*
16 Sullivan, *op. cit.*
17 *BPP* 1846 (530) XIII. 425, qq. 3056–7.
18 *BPP* 1856 (332) XII.1. q. 3926.
19 *BPP* 1846 (530) XIII. 425, q. 1885.
20 Published in Bernard Forest de Belidor, *La Science des Ingenieurs dans la Conduite des Travaux de Fortification et d'Architecture Civile* (Paris, 1729).
21 In a paper presented to L'Academie des Sciences, published in 1776.
22 S.P. Timoshenko, *History of Strength of Materials* (1953), p. 210. The brief explanation of the theories of Belidor and Coulomb is derived from Timoshenko pp. 47–51, 60–2. Civil Engineering undergraduates learn an updated version of Coulomb's theory to this day.
23 For the problems at Birkenhead Docks see K. McCarron, *op. cit.*
24 John Ellacot, 'Description of the Low Water Basin at Birkenhead', *Min. Proc. ICE*, vol. XXXIII (1869), pp. 518–35.
25 A. Giles, 'On the Construction of the Southampton Docks', *Min. Proc. ICE*, vol. XVII (1858), pp. 540–54. Rawlinson's contribution is at p. 552.
26 Peter Barlow's book has a tortured bibliography: it began as *An Essay on the Strength & Stress of Timber* (1817), and acquired many alterations and

additions, by no means all of them by Barlow, and ended as a posthumous edition worked up by his son, *A Treatise on the Strength of Materials* (1867). It appears to be that edition which so offended Baker. The first edition of W.J.M. Rankine *A Manual of Civil Engineering* was published in London in 1862 but it remained in print literally for decades.

27 *Min. Proc. ICE*, vol. LXV (1880–1), pp. 140–241.

28 See N. Ritchie-Noakes, *Jesse Hartley* (Liverpool, 1980), for description and illustrations.

29 A. Jarvis, 'An Attempt at a Bibliography of Samuel Smiles', *Industrial Archaeology Review*, vol. XII, No. 2 (spring 1991), pp. 162–71 gives details.

30 R.A. Buchanan, *The Engineers: A History of the Engineering Profession in Britain* (1989). His most telling point is the way in which successive generations of biographers have turned repeatedly to the same subjects.

Chapter Four Obsolescence, Railways and Coal

1 Eng. Rep. 1848–51.

2 Eng. Rep. 1855.

3 This and other complaints in Legal File A7/11. Details of Bibby vessels from E.W. Paget-Tomlinson, *The History of the Bibby Line* (Liverpool, 1969), pp. 64–5.

4 D&Q 13 June 1866.

5 The minutes of these decisions appear in sequence in WUP 29/1.

6 For traffic on the Leeds & Liverpool Canal see: M. Clarke, *The Leeds & Liverpool Canal* (Preston, 1990).

7 Eng. Rep. for those years.

8 Dionysius Lardner, *Railway Economy* (1850), p. 71.

9 *Report of the Dock Surveyors on a Proposed Plan of High Level Railway upon the Quays of Liverpool Docks* (Liverpool, 1853), p. 5.

10 This, together with much other mind-boggling bureaucracy, is detailed in BPP 1856 (332) XII.1. This example is from Appendix 4.

11 These proceedings are minuted in the early part of WUP 34/1.

12 T.R. Gourvish, 'Railways 1830–70: The Formative Years', M.J. Freeman and D.H. Aldcroft (eds), *Transport in Victorian Britain* (Manchester, 1988), p. 70.

13 SCW 2 March 1852.

14 While inside sources suggest that the work was willingly undertaken, a quite different view emerges from the evidence of Thomas Part, a coal-owner, in *BPP* 1856 (332) XII.1. qq. 3559 *et seq.*

15 The sequence of complaints and the reports and minutes in response is in WUP 34/1.

16 Traffic, 8 October 1879.

17 Certainly such fears were expressed to, and acknowledged by, the Joint Select Committee on Railway Amalgamation which was prompted by this attempted merger, *BPP* 1872 (364) XIII.

18 For the histories of these undertakings and their interests on the Mersey see: M. Clarke *op. cit*, C. Hadfield & G. Biddle, *Canals of the North West* (Newton Abbot, 1970), and A. Jarvis, *Ellesmere Port – Canal Town* (Ellesmere Port, 1977).

19 Works, 25 May 1880.
20 UWUP C127.
21 Eng. Rep. 1882–6.
22 F. Huddleston, 'The Coal Shipping Appliances of the Port of Liverpool', *TLES*, 1887, pp. 75–84.
23 *BPP* 1898 (366) LXXXII.251.
24 For relative merits of different coals, see H.S. Jevons, *The British Coal Trade* (1915), rep. (Newton Abbot, 1969), Chapter Three.
25 M. Clarke, *op. cit*, pp. 149–50.
26 Estimated figures for coal consumption are taken from invitations to tender for supply to the Board in WUP 100/1.
27 Though, according to Jevons (*op. cit*, p. 683), this reflected a relative stagnation in the Lancashire coalfield.

Chapter Five New Traffic, but the Same Old Story

1 Editorial article, 'Nelson Line's 42 Years', *Sea Breezes*, vol. 40, (October 1966), pp. 706–22 gives a brief history of the firm and a fuller account of its ships.
2 Minutes of the various decisions recounted here are collected in WUP 152/1.
3 For the history of meat imports to the Mersey see: K. McCarron, *Meat at Woodside: The Birkenhead Livestock Trade*, Merseyside Port Folios, (1991).
4 See C. Box, (ed. A. Jarvis), *The Liverpool Overhead Railway 1893–1956* (Shepperton, 1984).
5 These and other Board decisions on matters of property are minuted in WUP 59/2.
6 D&Q 14 August 1861. In 1876 the procedure was reconsidered, and re-adopted, adding Nelson to the list of docks included, D&Q 12 April 1876.
7 See *Lloyds List* for those dates.
8 P.S. Bagwell & J. Armstrong, 'Coastal Shipping' in Freeman & Aldcroft *op. cit*, p. 174.
9 See D.H. Aldcroft, *Studies in British Transport History 1870–1970*, Chapter Six.
10 Report of Board Meeting in *Liverpool Courier* 22 October 1897.
11 For a detailed history of Princes Dock see: A. Jarvis, *Princes Dock*, Merseyside Port Folios, (1991).
12 Bagwell & Armstrong *op. cit*, Table 6.
13 *Report of the Dock Surveyors on a Proposed Plan of High Level Railway upon the Quays of Liverpool Docks* (Liverpool, 1835), p. 5.
14 All these improvements, and others similar, are detailed in the sequence of UWUPs known as Berth Papers, filed in alphabetical order by the name of the tenant of the appropriated berth in question.

Chapter Six Matters of Moment

1 Works, 2 November 1883.
2 Although, of course, the evidence in the Lynch case (Legal Files E6 & E7) suggests that it was not necessarily accurate.

3 This appears to have happened in the case of the High Level Railway Extension, see Chapter Four.
4 Eng. Rep. 1865.
5 Eng. Rep. 1866.
6 Much of the considerable paperwork on the subject is in UWUP V19.
7 *Liverpool Telegraph*, 13 January 1879.
8 Works, 27 May 1879.
9 WUP 36/1 and UWUP 02a relate to huts and cocoa vans. See also the story of Ismay, Imrie's huts at West Waterloo, Chapter Seven.
10 This paragraph is based on minutes in WUP 9/1.
11 *Special Committee to Consider Dock Accommodation, 1871*, in Liv. RO H387.1 MER.
12 Dated 12 March 1883. A copy appears, surprisingly, in Liv. RO, Cotton Exchange Cuttings Book, 1929–53.
13 Recorded in the verbatim sequence Discussions at the Board for 15, 22 and 29 January 1891. The report itself is in Legal File H80.
14 Royal Commission in Labour. *BPP* 1892 (6708-v) XXXV.I. See, for example, evidence of William Beckett Hill, q. 6403 *et seq.*
15 Board, 14 March 1890. This incident also shows why the Board needed twenty-eight committee clerks.
16 This sequence of minutes is in WUP 59/3.
17 In evidence for the 1906 Bill, Lyster stated that he had effectively been engineer-in-chief since 1891. Legal File A87.

Chapter Seven Odd Man Out: East Waterloo Dock

1 All the Agreements referred to in this paragraph are in Agreements Book for the dates mentioned in the text.
2 Figures extracted from Hyde Appendices and MDHB Pocket Book.
3 Dates in this paragraph refer to DCM.
4 Petition for the Bill of 1854, Legal File A7.
5 Reports of the astronomer to The Observatory Committee were printed and published and survive in Liv. RO. The 1850 report contains a recapitulation of the history of the observatory to that date, upon which this paragraph is based.
6 MDHB Register of Employees SW1/2 provides a brief record of appointments and salaries.
7 Astronomer's Report 1849.
8 Published as R. Sheepshanks, *Correspondence respecting the Liverpool Observatory between Mr John Taylor and the Revd R. Sheepshanks* (1845).
9 Astronomer's Reports for 1855 and 1857.
10 N. Longmate, *The Bread Stealers* (NY and London, 1984), provides a readable account and a useful bibliography.
11 P. Westmacott, 'Description of the Hydraulic Machinery for Warehousing Grain at the Liverpool Docks'. *Proc. IME* 1869, pp. 208–28.
12 Royal Commission on Labour, *BPP* 1892 (6708 -v) XXXV.1, Evidence of Josiah Griffin, q. 6080 *et seq.*

13 Goodwin, 'Appliances for the Inland Transport and Manipulation of Bulk Grain', *Journal of the Liverpool Polytechnic Society*, 1878, pp. 47–61. (The Society did not give forenames or initials to its contributors.)
14 The account of the equipment which follows is largely derived from Westmacott *op. cit.*
15 TCW ledger for dates given in text.
16 Figures from Eng. Rep. for the years 1864–72.
17 See MRC's handlist of drawings for the quantity of last-minute work.
18 Note that Westmacott had stated its original capacity as 21 cwt. His figures are not to be relied upon: at p. 212 he states that the pumps were capable of delivering 209,350 cu ft/min of water at 700 lb/in^2. That represents an engine power of over 2,500,000 hp!
19 Works, 19 March 1869.
20 Works, 5 June 1871.
21 Warehouses Committee, 31 July 1876.
22 Works, 28 July 1876.
23 Reported in *Liverpool Daily Courier* 7 December 1883.
24 Letter: Insurers to Warehouse Committee 3 December 1874.
25 W. Pilkington on the 'Elevation, Storage and Shipment of Grain', *Min. Proc. ICE* LXXVII (1883–4), pp. 237–46.
26 *Special Committee to Consider Dock Accommodation*, 1871–2, evidence of Mr Cunliffe, Liv. RO H387.1 MER.
27 This report, dated 14 January 1890, appears in WUP 95/1.
28 Eng. Rep. 1889.
29 Eng. Rep. 1893.
30 Contract approved by Warehouse Committee 16 October 1895; instruction to solicitor 12 February 1896, in WUP 95/1.
31 Figures from evidence for 1898 Dock Bill. Legal File A7.
32 Legal File H80.
33 UWUP EI3.

Chapter Eight A Day in the Life of a Dock

1 The description of the William Dock up to this point is loosely based on Clarence Dock.
2 The rubbish boats' berth was at NE Collingwood. At an unknown date in the '90s a loading conveyor was installed which reduced the drudgery but not the unpleasantness.
3 Disputes over depths of water were frequent. Since this group of docks was not fully impounded (i.e. passage gates were opened through at high water) the levels varied, making the disputes as inconclusive as they were costly. Examples may be found in WUP 9/1.
4 The account of the canteen is based on that built at the main dockyard.
5 For many interesting sidelights on the grain trade see: G.J.S. Broomhall & J.H. Hubback, *Corn Trade Memories, Recent and Remote* (Liverpool, 1930).

6 Cranes of this type may be seen in photographs of, for example, Clarence and East Canning Docks.
7 Minor bribery such as this was endemic. Instant dismissal in case of acceptance was ordered by the Dock Committee 22 December 1836. Earlier still, there had been allegations of much more serious bribery: Charles Parnell, dockmaster at Georges dock, was said to have received individual payments of £50 (a third of his legitimate salary) on more than one occasion. It was, however, almost impossible to control lumpers, stevedores etc. who were employed by contractors.
8 The description of this building is based on the East Princes Dock half-tide shed.
9 Stranger than fiction, this statue still exists, and I thank the Art & Architecture Department of the Archdiocesan Liturgical Commission for the anecdote.
10 Oral evidence gathered by the author in Ellesmere Port in 1976.
11 By 1890, few sailing vessels used the Central Docks, with the exception of flats, occasional small ocean-going vessels at Princes and a few long-haul grain ships at East Waterloo.
12 For dealings involving cocoa vans see UWUP O2[a].
13 Derived from Lynch's confession and other draft depositions in Legal File E6. See also Chapter Two above.
14 A sequence of UWUPs dealing with 'Irregularities' includes occasional prosecutions. They occur in infrequent clusters, indicating a norm of tolerance interrupted by occasional purges. This parallels a tolerance shown in earlier days when minor thefts were often prosecuted under bye-law rather than as felonies. The 'Furnaces' were first ordered by the Dock Committee 26 March 1837 following complaints of the activities of female scavengers taking firewood from Clarence Graving Dock.
15 Awards made during the later period of the Charitable Fund are detailed in WUP 148/1.
16 This rivalry may be seen in WUP 36/1. Relations began to improve after the appointment of A.G. Lyster as engineer in 1897, but progress was slow.
17 For the decision-making required in dockmasters and their staff, see Alan Johnson, *Working the Tides* (Liverpool, 1988).
18 Vulgar entertainment of this kind in Liverpool is ill-documented. For a general view see K. Chesney, *The Victorian Underworld* (1970).
19 For places he might have been, see Anthea Jarvis, *Liverpool Fashion: Its Makers and Wearers* (Liverpool, 1981).
20 Official records do not cover the skills of such as our fictitious bosun, which can only be discovered by watching the increasingly rare manipulation of unpowered craft in the docks. In this context it may be remarked that most sail training vessels 'cheat', not only with auxiliary motors but even using high-powered inflatables as 'bow thrusters' when berthing.

Chapter Nine The Future as Seen in 1905

1 Figures from Hyde, Appendix 1.
2 Board 15 December 1904, reported in *Jnl Comm.* 16 December.

3 1906 Dock Bill, evidence of J.W. Hughes before House of Commons Committee, Legal File A87.
4 WUP 60/1904.
5 Royal Commission to enquire into the subject of the administration of the Port of London and other matters connected therewith. *BPP* 1902 (1151) XL 111. 222.
6 *Jnl Comm.* 21 October 1904.
7 *Jnl Comm.* 26 October 1904 and *Mercury* 8 November 1904 respectively.
8 For details of the Princes Dock shoe-string see A.E. Jarvis. *Princes Dock*, Merseyside Port Folios, 1991, Chapters Three and Four.
9 Discussions at Board 16 November 1905.
10 *Mercury* 5 November 1904.
11 *Mercury* 9 November 1904.
12 A copy of the competition rules appears in WUP 93/1.
13 1906 Dock Bill, evidence of A.G. Lyster before House of Commons Committee Legal File A87.
14 These figures were much bandied around by George Cox (of the Chamber of Commerce) and others, but they assumed a par issue of stock at 3 per cent or less, underwritten by the corporation. The Board, probably rightly, would not consider such an arrangement, fearing interference, and in those circumstances the estimated saving was hopelessly optimistic.
15 These agonized proceedings appear in Discussions at Board for 19 December and 29 December 1904.
16 The story of *Galatea* is in WUP 158/1.

BIBLIOGRAPHY

The bibliography which follows makes no attempt to be exhaustive. It contains only publications which are cited in the notes together with a handful of works which have been found helpful as background information but have not been cited. The reader who desires more is referred to the bibliographies of Hyde and Ritchie-Noakes. A few entries have been added below for works of more general interest published since 1984.

Aldcroft, D.H. (ed.), *Studies in British Transport History* (Newton Abbot, 1956).

Anon. (editorial), 'Nelson Line's 42 Years', *Sea Breezes*, vol. 40 (October 1966), pp. 706–22.

Anon. (J. and J.B. Hartley), Report of the Dock Surveyors on a Proposed Plan of High Level Railway upon the Quays of the Liverpool Docks (Liverpool, 1853).

Anon. (J. Hartnup), *Reports of the Astronomer to the Observatory Committee* (Liverpool, 1849–57).

Anstey, R. and Hair, P.E.H. (eds), *Liverpool, the African Slave Trade and Abolition* (Liverpool, 1976).

Baker, B., 'On the Actual Lateral Pressure of Earthworks', *Min. Proc. ICE*, LXV (1880–1), pp. 140–241.

Banckes, J.H.M. and Harris, J.R., 'The First Lancashire Locomotive', *Journal of Transport History*, 5 (1961–2), pp. 146–8.

Barker, T.C. and Harris, J.R., *A Merseyside Town in the Industrial Revolution* (Liverpool, 1954).

Barlow, P., *A Treatise on the Strength of Materials* (1867).

Booth, H., *Henry Booth* (Ilfracombe, 1980).

Broadbridge, S.R., 'John Pinkerton and the Birmingham Canals' *Transport History*, 4 (1971) pp. 33–49.

Broomhall, G.J.S. and Hubback, J.H., *Corn Trade Memories, Recent and Remote* (Liverpool, 1930).

Box, C., *The Liverpool Overhead Railway*, ed. A. Jarvis (Shepperton, 1984).

Buchanan, R.A., *The Engineers: A History of the Engineering Profession in Britain* (1989).

Burton, V. (ed.), *Liverpool Shipping, Trade and Industry* (Liverpool, 1989).

Chesney, K., *The Victorian Underworld* (1970).
Clarke, M., *The Leeds and Liverpool Canal* (Preston, 1990).
Coleman, T., *The Railway Navvies* (Harmondsworth, 1968).
Ellacot, J., 'Description of the Low Water Basin at Birkenhead', *Min. Proc. ICE*, XXXIII (1869), pp. 518–35.
Fraser, D., *Power and Authority in the Victorian City* (Oxford, 1979).
Freeman, M.J. and Aldcroft, D.H. (eds), *Transport in Victorian Britain* (Manchester, 1988).
Giles, A., 'On the Construction of Southampton Docks', *Min. Proc. ICE*, XVII (1858), pp. 540–54.
Goodwin, ?, 'Appliances for the Inland Transport and Manipulation of Grain', *Journal of the Liverpool Polytechnic Society 1878*, pp. 47–61.
Hadfield, C. and Biddle, G., *Canals of the North West* (Newton Abbot, 1970).
Hoon, E., *The English Customs Service 1696–1786* (New York, 1938).
Huddleston, F., 'The Coal Shipping Appliances of the Port of Liverpool', *TLES*, 1887, pp. 75–84.
Hyde, F.E., *Liverpool and the Mersey* (Newton Abbot, 1980).
Jarvis, A., *Ellesmere Port: Canal Town* (Ellesmere Port, 1977).
——, *Princes Dock* (Liverpool, 1991).
——, 'An Attempt at a Bibliography of Samuel Smiles', *Industrial Archaeology Review*, XIII 2 (spring 1991), pp. 162– 71.
——, 'The Interests and Ethics of John Foster, Liverpool Dock Surveyor', *THSLC*, 1991 (forthcoming).
——, 'Harold Littledale, The Man with a Mission', in ed. H.M. Hignett, *A Second Merseyside Maritime History* (Liverpool, 1991).
Jarvis, A.M., *Liverpool Fashion: Its makers and wearers* (Liverpool, 1981).
Jevons, H.S., *The British Coal Trade (1915)* (repr, Newton Abbot, 1969).
Johnson, A., *Working the Tides* (Liverpool, 1988).
Keith-Lucas, B., *The Unreformed Local Government System* (1980).
Lardner, D., *Railway Economy* (1850).
Longmate, N., *The Bread Stealers* (1984).
Lyster, G.F., *The History of the Birkenhead Great Low Water Basin* (Liverpool, 1864).
McCarron, K., *The Fall and Rise of Birkenhead Docks* (Liverpool, 1991, forthcoming).
——, *Meat at Woodside; The Birkenhead Livestock Trade* (Liverpool, 1991).
Paget-Tomlinson, E.W., *The History of the Bibby Line* (Liverpool, 1969).
Parkinson, C.N., *The Rise of the Port of Liverpool* (Liverpool, 1952).
Penfold, A. (ed.), *Thomas Telford, Engineer* (1980).
Pilkington, W., 'On the Elevation, Storage and Shipment of Grain', *Min. Proc. ICE*, LXXVII (1883–4), pp. 237–46.
Rankine, W.J.M., *A Manual of Civil Engineering* (1862).
Return of the Number of Accidents which have occurred during shunting operations to employees on the Railways of the UK during the ten years ending 1897, *BPP*, 1898 (366) LXXXII.251.
Rideout, E.H., 'The Development of the Liverpool Warehousing System', *THSLC*, 82 (1930) 1/41.

BIBLIOGRAPHY

Ritchie-Noakes, N., *Jesse Hartley* (Liverpool, 1980).
——, *Liverpool's Historic Waterfront* (1984).
Royal Commission on Labour, *BPP*, 1892 (6708) XXXV.1.
Royal Commission to enquire into the subject of the administration of the Port of London, *BPP*, 1902 (1151) XLIII.222.
Select Committee on Local Charges on Shipping in Ports of UK, *BPP*, 1856 (332) XII.1.
Select Committee on Railway Labourers, *BPP*, 1846 (530) XIII.425.
Sheepshanks, R., *Correspondence respecting the Liverpool Observatory between Mr John Taylor and the Revd R. Sheepshanks* (1845).
Slatcher, W.N., 'The Barnsley Canal: its first twenty Years', *Transport History*, 1 (1968), pp. 48–66.
Spiegl, F. (ed.), *An Everyday History of Liverpool* (Liverpool, UD).
Sullivan, D., *Navvyman* (1983).
Timoshenko, S.P., *History of the Strength of Materials* (1953).
Thomas, R.H.G., *The Liverpool and Manchester Railway* (Newton Abbot, 1980).
Troughton, T., *The History of Liverpool* (Liverpool, 1810).
Westmacott, P., 'Description of the Machinery for Warehousing Grain at the Liverpool Docks', *Proc. IME*, 1869, pp. 206–28.

INDEX

This index sets out to give quite full entries for names of docks and persons, as well as for a number of key themes. It does not attempt, however, to list every mention of the main decision-making bodies, principally the Liverpool Council, its Dock Committee, and the Mersey Docks and Harbour Board. Their story is so integral to the theme of the book that it is not really practical to go 'dipping' for it. References to Chapter Eight have been confined to a handful of important topics (for example, refuse trade) which are mentioned only there.

The page references in italics refer to illustrations.

INDEX

INDEX

INDEX

INDEX